Kings & Things

Published by Galore Park Publishing Ltd
19/21 Sayers Lane
Tenterden
Kent TN30 6BW
www.galorepark.co.uk

The text of this abridged edition is copyright © Galore Park 2006
Illustrations copyright © Galore Park 2006

This edition first published 2006

Designed and typeset by Design Gallery, Suffolk
Illustrations by Matthew Rice
Text abridged by Lucy Hume

Printed by Butler and Tanner

ISBN-13 978 1 902984 84 1
ISBN-10 1 902984 84 6

Also by H.E. Marshall published by Galore Park Publishing
Our Island Story
Scotland's Story

T

Kings & Things

First Stories from English History

by H.E. Marshall

Illustrated by Matthew Rice

www.galorepark.co.uk

☞ Preface ☜

These stories of English history have been written in the
hope that Mothers and Nannies and other great Potentates
of Nursery Land will read them to their obedient Subjects in
the Story Hour which so often precedes the tragic necessity of
'going to bed'. In such an hour small people are often beguiled
with fairy-tales, with myths and legends. But the most interesting
story of all - the story of their own Country - is not infrequently
neglected. It is so neglected because it is thought to be a story
too frightening or too difficult for the very young person's
understanding.

In this Outline of English history, therefore, I have not dwelt
on horror or on the glory of bloodshed. But ours is a rough story,
and when such matters could not altogether be avoided they have
been passed over as lightly as possible.

The style I may add is copied largely from that of some very
young friends who have been in the habit of telling me stories.
I hope that it will appeal to others of a like age.

There are no dates throughout the text. A few are given at the
end of the book as a slight guide to the 'Grown Ups' in the event
of uncomfortable questions being asked.

H.E. Marshall

Contents

Chapter		*page*

SPQR

Ever and ever so long ago there was a Very Important King kind of person called Julius. He lived in Rome and ruled all the Romans. He was a very Conquering kind of person too. So he began to conquer all the people he knew, for their own good. Because, he said, "The Romans know far more than anyone else and are far more clever than the others, so it will do them good to be conquered and taught things. Besides, when we have conquered them we can make them work for Us and we can take all their gold and things, so we will have a lot more money and fun too." So Julius went out Conquering.

Now one day he heard of a little Island called Britain across the Sea and he thought he would go and conquer it.

When the Britons saw lots and lots of boats come rowing toward the shore, they didn't like the look of them.

"Here are a lot of Conquering People coming to fight us," they said; "let's get ready."

So they hung their best gold chains round their necks and put on their best fur coats and got out their War Carriages which had wheels all stuck round with Sharp Knives ready to cut the Foe to pieces.

So when Julius landed he got the kind of Welcome he didn't expect. The Britons fought like anything and lots of people got killed.

Julius didn't like it much, and after a bit he sailed away.

Next year he came back again with lots more ships and lots more men, for he had learned his Lesson: That Britons Are Not Easy To Beat.

There were lots and lots of Battles and Fightings and goings on. Then Julius took some prisoners and went away.

For about a Hundred Years after this the Britons were left in Peace. Then another Important King kind of person thought he would do some more Conquering in Britain. His name was Claudius. Claudius found the Britons just as Hard-to-Beat as Julius had done. One of the Hardest-to-Beat was a great Prince called Caractacus. He was a very Brave Man and perhaps he wouldn't have been beaten at all. Only, he was Betrayed by a Friend, so it was easy for Claudius to take him and his wife and children prisoners and carry them off to Rome.

When he got home, to make people believe that he had conquered Britain, he made Caractacus walk in a Procession with handcuffs on his wrists and clanking iron chains round his ankles.

When the Show was over Claudius sent for Caractacus and said, "Now you see what you get for fighting against me. I've conquered you and you are my slave."

But Caractacus answered as Bold as anything, "You haven't conquered me. You had me Betrayed and I'm not your slave, for

Britons Never, Never Will Be Slaves. Kill me if you like; you can't make me a slave."

Instead of getting into a Towering Rage Claudius was quite pleasant. Instead of saying "Off with his head," he said, "Off with those iron chains." And Caractacus was once more a Free Man. But whether he got back to his dear Britain or not I don't know. I rather suspect that he died of a Broken Heart in a Foreign Land.

As well as Brave Men who fought against the Romans there were Brave Women too. And one of the Bravest was Queen Boadicea. She gathered her people together and spoke to them in such Proud, Brave Words that they became as bold as Lions and eager to fight for their Queen and Country. So they fought and fought and very nearly beat the Romans.

But there were far more Romans, and they had been taught how to fight, while the Britons were just Brave Men fighting to keep their Own Country Free. So at last there was a great Big Fight when hundreds and hundreds of Britons were killed. And when only about the Last Man was left standing Boadicea was very sad.

So she took a cup and filled it up with Poison and drank it. And when the Roman soldiers burst into her tent they found the Lovely Lady lying dead.

But there seemed No End of Romans and they kept coming and coming and Conquering and Conquering until they had conquered a good bit of the Island. Then they built grand houses and did all the Ruling and were the Most Important Persons.

That went on for hundreds of years. Then the Romans began to have a lot of Bothers at Home. So they said, "We have to have such a lot of soldiers here to keep order and we need all our soldiers at Home. We had much better go Home and take all our soldiers with us." And off they went.

The Britons were jolly glad to see the last of them. The Romans had Taught them a lot of things – how to make good roads, and build stone houses, and cut their hair and take Baths, and learn Latin, and a lot of other things. But the Britons weren't a bit grateful. It just seemed Hard Lines to have to be taught as well as conquered. So they said Good Riddance to Bad Rubbish.

CHAPTER II · SAXON CONQUERINGS

The Britons sang with Joy when the Romans went, but they soon changed their Tune.

There were terrible Wild Men called Picts and Scots who lived in the North parts of the Island. The Romans had built a great, big Wall to keep them out. But now that there were no Romans to guard the Wall, these Picts and Scots came climbing over it like anything, stealing things and smashing everything they could lay hands on.

They were such a Bother that the Britons actually asked the Romans to come back again. But they said, "No, thank you. We have quite enough Bothers at Home. You must just look after yourselves now."

Then all the most Important People among the Britons began quarrelling. Ever so many of them wanted to be King and things got into a jolly fine Mess.

At last one of them got to be a bit more Important than the others. So he said, "We can't have all these Goings-On. There are some people called Saxons who live across the sea. I'm told that they are awfully good at fighting. Let's send and ask them to give us a hand. I'm sure they will if we say we'll pay them well."

So they asked the Saxons to come, and the Saxons said, "Thank you very much. We'd like nothing better." Then two of their Important People gathered their soldiers together and sailed over to Britain. One of these Important People was called Hengist and the other was called Horsa, and both their names mean Horse, so I expect they were as strong as horses.

They gave the Picts and Scots a good Licking, and the Britons paid them and said, "Thank you very much," and expected them to go Home again.

But Hengist and Horsa didn't go. "This is a jolly fine Country," they said, "let's stay here."

Then more and more people came from over the sea, Saxons and Angles and Jutes, and they went Rampaging and Conquering all over the Island. The Saxons, however, didn't find it an Easy Job to conquer the Britons. There were lots and lots of Fightings and Battles all over the place. And there was one special Famous King called Arthur who beat them over and over again and kept them at Bay.

Arthur was fifteen when he began being King. He was as Brave as a Lion and as Gentle as a Lamb. But although he could fight like anything, and thought that people should be Brave, he liked them to have Good Manners too. "Look," he said, "you needn't be rude, although you are strong. If you are you will just become Big Bullies and I won't have Big Bullies in my Army. And you mustn't be Sneaks either and Tell Tales about each other for I won't listen to them. And you mustn't fight with women and girls but be gentle and respect them. And never Tell Lies."

Then, so that they couldn't fight about a little thing like getting the Best Place at Table, he made a Big Round Table for all his Best Knights to sit at so that no knight could say he had a Better Place than another.

Arthur was Gentle like that in Peace Time. But in War he was Terrible. When he had girt on his Sword Excalibur, and taken in hand his great Spear Ron, the Saxons fled before him.

But at length Arthur was killed, and all the other British Kings who fought against the Saxons were killed too. So when the Saxons had finished their Conquerings the people weren't Britons any longer but English, and then Britain became England.

CHAPTER III · ENGLAND CONQUERED for CHRIST

When the Romans first came to Britain they were Pagans and so were the Britons; because Jesus Christ hadn't been Born into the World by then. So of course they couldn't know about Him. It wasn't until years and years and years later that they knew anything about Him.

Then someone came and told them the Wonderful Story and lots and lots of Britons became Christians. But after a bit an Important Person in Rome began to hate the Christians and wanted to kill them all. So the Soldiers were told to and they began killing them.

When the Romans went away lots and lots of Britons had become Christians. Then the Saxons and Angles and Jutes came, and *they* were all Heathens who knew nothing about Jesus Christ and the True God. So they robbed the Churches and pulled them down and burned them up until the Wonderful Story was forgotten in all England and the Name of Christ unknown.

Then one day a Good Man called Gregory was walking through the Market at Rome when he saw some children put there to be sold for Slaves. For in those times they used to sell people as we do sheep and cows.

These children had fair hair, rosy cheeks, and blue eyes, and Gregory thought he'd never seen such pretty children.

"Where do those children come from?" he asked.

"From England," said the Man who was selling them; "they are Angles."

"Oh," said Gregory, "they shouldn't be called Angles, but Angels, they are so Pretty."

Then he asked more about them and was told that they were little Heathens and that all the People of England were Heathens too.

"Oh, what a pity," said Gregory; "I must buy them and teach them to be Good Christians." So he bought them.

When Gregory had taught the children to be Good Christians they told him lots about England. And Gregory liked it so much that he said, "I must really go to England and teach them to be Good Christians like I have these children."

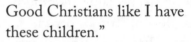

So he asked the Pope, "Can I go to England and teach the People there to be Good Christians?"

But the People at Rome were Awfully Fond of Gregory, and they made such a Fuss that the Pope said, "I think you'd better not go."

Then one day, Gregory being such a Good Man and the people at Rome being so Fond of him, they made him Pope.

"Now," thought Gregory, "as I'm made Pope I can't ever go
to England. I must stay in Rome and look after Things here, but
I can send someone else to teach them to be Good Christians."

So he told a Good Man called Augustine to go and to take
a lot of other Good Men with him to help him.

Now at this time England wasn't all under one King as it is
now. The Angles and Saxons and Jutes had chopped it all up into
bits and there were about seven Kings all ruling in England at
one time, each having his own Little Bit.

The first Kingdom Augustine came to was the Kingdom of
Kent. So he stopped there for a bit, and baptized the King and
made him a Good Christian, and lots of the people too. And
as years and years went on lots and lots more Good Men came
to help them. So at last all England belonged to the Church
of Christ.

After the Angles and Saxons and Jutes had finished all their Conquerings they thought they'd rest a bit and have some Peace and Quiet. But across the Sea there were more fierce Wild Men called Danes.

Just as the Romans had done, these Wild Danes heard that England was a fine Rich Country. So they said, "Come on. Let's go and get some gold and silver and things."

Then they got into their Long Boats and came dashing over the Sea to England. When they got there they just killed some people, stole everything they could lay hands on, set fire to the houses, and dashed away again. They didn't come like the Romans to teach people anything, or like the Saxons to find New Homes. They came just for the Fun; it was like an Outing or a Weekend Party for them.

Over and over again the Danes came, and more and more of them came. Then some of them said, "What's the good of going backwards and forwards across the Sea? England is a fine Country; let's stay." So they stayed. They turned some of the English out of their homes and treated them like Dirt beneath their feet and were Very Proud and Haughty.

But the English didn't take it all quietly. "These Danes are a Perfect Nuisance," they said, "we must Do Something." So they got out their swords and things and fought like anything. But it didn't seem to make much difference, for more and more came sailing over the sea.

So it went on for years and years. At last the English got a very clever King called Alfred. He gathered all his men together and fought a great Big Battle. The English fought and fought until there was only about One Man left Standing. And when there's only One Man left Standing you can't go on fighting, so Alfred went away and lived in a Cow-man's cottage till he could Think Things Out. And he said to the Cow-man, "Don't tell anyone who I am, for I don't want the Danes to know till I've Thought Things Out."

The Cow-man was a Faithful Follower, so he didn't even tell his wife. Of course a King doesn't know anything about Helping in the House. Besides, Alfred had lots to do just Thinking. But the Wife didn't know that and she thought that Alfred was a Lazy Fellow sitting there all day long doing nothing and making a Lot More Work for her to do. So she grumbled like anything.

One day she was very busy. She had baked some scones and had Lots of other things to do. "Well," she said to herself, "I've only One Pair of Hands and I can't do Everything. Surely this Lazy Fellow could make himself useful for Once." Then out loud she said, "Here, just you look after my scones while I'm gone, and don't let them burn."

"All right," said the King; "I'll look after them."

But as soon as the Wife had gone he forgot all about them and went on with his Thinking. And when the Wife came back her scones were burned to cinders. She was so angry that she boxed his ears and scolded him like anything. She was still scolding when the Cow-man came in. He was shocked at her!

"Hold your tongue, Woman!" he shouted. But she still went on. "Shut up won't you?" he cried out at last; "don't you know you're talking to the King!"

The King! Well! That did shut her up.

At last the King had done his Thinking and gathered his Faithful Followers again. Then they fought the Danes like anything, and in a Big Battle Alfred conquered them altogether. Alfred didn't banish all the Danes who had come to Stay. But he made them all live in one place and Behave Properly and not treat the English like Dirt under their Feet. And there was Peace in the Land.

After being a grand Fighter Alfred became a Great Ruler. He made Good Laws and saw that people Obeyed them. He built schools, he built ships, and kept the Good Peace, so everybody loved him till one day he died.

That was a sad day for England, for as soon as the Danes heard the news they said, "Come on, King Alfred's dead. Let's go and do some more plundering in England."

So it all began over again, and all the English Kings, good ones and bad ones, had to fight them for years and years. But even the Best Kings weren't as good at fighting them as Alfred, and the bold, bad Danes got bolder and badder.

Then the English had a Stupid King called Ethelred the Unready, because he could never make up his mind about anything. He got frightened of the Danes and ran away to France, and things went on getting worse and worse. At length some of the English said, "It's No Use fighting these Danes any longer. We may as well Give In and have Peace." So they went to a Very Clever Dane called Canute and said, "You can be King if you like and we won't fight against you any more."

But others wouldn't have Canute; and they chose an English King called Edmund. He was such a strong man that he was called Edmund Ironsides. So there were a lot of Battles between Edmund's men and Canute's men.

At last Edmund got tired of having such a lot of his Fine Men killed. So he said to Canute, "Look here, what's the good of all this Killing? It isn't Sense. It would be far better if you and I had a fight between ourselves. If you kill me then you can be King and if I kill you then I'll be King."

So they began their Fight. But Edmund was a Great, Big, Strong Man and Canute was just Ordinary, and Canute soon saw that Most Likely he'd get killed. So he yelled out, "Look here,

don't let's fight any more! Let's divide the Kingdom between us."
They shook hands and shared the Kingdom and settled it that
if one of them died the other should have it all. And very soon
Edmund died and Canute the Dane was King all by himself.

He wasn't a very Nice King to begin with but he got Quite
Good. Then some of the Important People thought they'd Curry
Favour with him and began to flatter him like anything.

Then one day Canute and some of the Most Important People
were walking by the Sea.

"Oh, what a Great King you are," said one. "Oh yes," said
another; "you can do anything you like. Even the waves would
obey you if you told them to stop."

"Do you think so?" said Canute. "Well, just bring my Golden
Chair and set it down here."

So they brought the King's Golden Chair, and Canute sat down close to the water where the tide was coming in.

"Now stop where you are," said Canute to the waves. "Don't you dare to come and wet my feet."

But of course the waves didn't pay any attention, and Canute got his feet wet.

Then Canute got up and looked sternly at the Important People round him. "Now you see how Silly you are," he said. "Don't let me hear any more Foolish Talk like that."

When Canute died two of his sons ruled after him. They were No Good at all and the English got tired of having Danish Kings. So they sent over to France and got the son of that King who had run away from the Danes. He was called Edward, but as he had lived nearly all his life in France he was fonder of the French than of the English.

Still it was a Great Thing to be King of England, so he came, and brought a lot of Frenchmen called Normans with him. These Normans were really Danes who had gone Conquering and Plundering in France. Some of these Danes made their Homes in France and became sort of French and called the land they took there, Normandy. But instead of having a King they had a Duke as their Most Important Person. This Duke was called William and he was King Edward's Cousin.

This Duke came to visit Edward. He thought England was a very Fine Country and that it would be a Grand Thing to be a King as well as a Duke, so he said to Edward, "Look here, when you die I wish you'd let me be King;" and Edward said, "Yes, of course you can, if you'd like to."

So they settled it like that, without asking the English People what *they* would like. But then Edward wasn't a Very First Class

Kind of King. He didn't think about the Good-of-the-People. He just liked to go his Own Way and do as he liked. He did like however building Churches and saying his Prayers and Confessing his Sins. So he was called Edward the Confessor.

After a bit a very clever Earl called Harold helped him to rule, so things got better, and the People loved Harold.

One day Harold went for a sail and an Awful Storm came on, so that he couldn't get back home, and his boat got wrecked on the coast of Normandy. Then Duke William got hold of him and wouldn't let him go Home until he'd promised to let him be King when Edward died.

"Oh dear!" thought Harold; "what am I to do? If I don't get home Edward will be doing all sorts of Things Wrong. I must get home."

So he said, "All right, you can be King," and William let him go Home. But Harold didn't mean what he said. He just said it so that he could get back to England. That was very Bad of him. For you musn't make a Promise and then break it.

Then, soon after Harold got back, King Edward went and died.

As soon as Edward died the People made Harold King although he wasn't really the Heir-to-the-Throne. But they loved him and were sure that he would be a Good King.

But when William heard that Harold had been made King of England he got into such an Awful Rage that even the Most Important People were afraid to go near him. Then he called all his Most Important People together and said, "Come on, we'll go to England and do some Conquering."

Harold too gathered his men together, and the two armies met at Hastings. It was a dreadful Battle. From morning till night they fought. Swords clashed and arrows flew. At length an arrow hit Good King Harold, whom the people loved so much, and he fell dead.

So William won the battle. After that he went Conquering and Conquering all over England, till the English saw that it was not Worth While fighting any more and they Gave In.

Then William gave Broad Lands and Grand Houses to the Normans. And they were very proud and haughty and the poor English had a Very Bad time.

Of course the English hated William like anything and thought everything he did was Bad and Cruel. But all the same he did some Good Things. He made a great Big Book, which he called the Domesday Book. In it he wrote the names of all the Great Houses and all the Broad Lands in All England and how much land each person had. So he had only to look in it to see where the Important People lived and how Rich they were. And after hundreds and hundreds of years we still have the Domesday Book and the names of some of our houses are still in it.

William was called William the Conqueror, and the Normans were the last people to come conquering in Britain.

William II. The King who was always Getting into Tempers

William the Conqueror thought it was a Grand Thing to be King of England, but he really thought it even still grander to be Duke of Normandy. So when he felt that he was going to die he told his eldest son Robert that he could be Duke of Normandy, and, "William," he said, "you can be King of England."

So off William went and got himself crowned. He was called the Red King because he had Red Hair. He was always getting into Tempers too, so he often had a Red Face as well.

William wasn't a bit a Nice Kind of King. He didn't care a bit about his people or about anything Good so long as he could just do what he liked.

The thing William liked best was to go hunting, and one morning he and all the Most Important People set off for a grand Hunt. In the evening they all got home again except the King and another man. Everyone began wondering what the King was doing staying out so late, until a poor farmer found him lying dead in the Forest with an Arrow sticking in his Heart. So he put him on his cart and took him to the Castle.

No one ever found out exactly how it happened, but everyone thought that the other man who didn't come back must have killed the King.

Anyhow the Red King was Dead and no one was sorry.

Henry I. The King who liked Reading and Writing

The next King was William's youngest brother, Henry. He had been born in England and that seemed to make him more like an Englishman. The English had hated both the Williams, for they were just Normans and couldn't even speak English.

"But," they said, "here now, this Henry, he was born in England, perhaps he'll be a bit better." And he was. He was a pleasant sort of Gentleman who liked to laugh and joke with people.

Henry wanted some Peace and Quiet so that he could read books and do things like that. But People didn't ever have much Peace and Quiet in those days and Henry and Robert soon began quarrelling. At last Henry went over to Normandy and gave Robert a good beating, made himself Duke of Normandy, and brought Robert back to England.

He put him in Prison and said, "Now you can just stay there and perhaps I'll get some Peace and Quiet." And there poor Robert stayed till he died.

But after the King of England began being Duke of Normandy too

it just made quarrels between the French and the English which went on for years and years and years.

But now the English began to have a much better time. Then Henry married Princess Matilda, who was the daughter of the King of Scotland. The English didn't love the Scots much for they still had lots of Bothers with them.

"However," said the English, "Princess Matilda is the Great-Granddaughter of Edmund Ironsides so that makes her nearly English."

But the Norman Lords turned up their noses at her. They thought it was an awful Come-down for *their* King to go marrying the Princess of a petty little Kingdom like Scotland. "Why couldn't he have married a Real Lady?" they asked – "a Normaness." So they weren't very kind to Queen Matilda. But perhaps she didn't pay much attention to them as she had her husband and her two children, William and Matilda, to look after.

Now that Henry was Duke of Normandy as well as King of England he was always going over to Normandy to see how things were getting on there. One time he took Prince William with him. He had finished his business and was all packed up ready to come home when a Sailor Man came to see him. "Please, Sir King," said the Sailor Man, "I have a lovely ship called the *White Ship*. It is all newly painted and as clean as anything; won't you sail over to England in it?"

"Oh, I can't do that," said King Henry; "I'm all packed up and ready to start. But Prince William is here too. He's having rather a good time and doesn't want to start yet. So I'll go on and you can bring him a little later in the day. But don't stay too late, William," he added

But Prince William was having such a good time that he forgot all about not staying too long, and it was quite late in the night before they started. The sailors too had been having a good time and they didn't pay much attention to where they were going. The Ship was sailing along quite gaily when all of a sudden there was a Terrible Crash. They had run right on to a sharp rock and made a great hole in the Ship and in a few minutes it sank down and down to the bottom of the sea. So everyone was drowned except one man. He was a Fat Butcher and had on a woolly sheepskin coat and that kept him from perishing of Cold.

Meanwhile at home Henry was growing anxious. Then he got rather angry and said, "I told him not to be late and here it is nearly midnight and no sign of him." At last King Henry gave it up and went to bed and tried to sleep.

In the morning, however, there was still no William there. But Henry wasn't angry any more, only dreadfully, dreadfully anxious, for he loved Prince William better than anyone else in the Whole Wide World.

King Henry couldn't imagine what had become of his son. But everyone else knew. For in the morning some Poor Fishermen found the Fat Butcher half dead with cold still clinging on to a bit of wood. And when he could speak he told them all that had happened.

Soon everyone had heard the news except the King. For he was sitting alone in his Castle and no one dared to go to tell him. Even the proud Norman Lords were afraid to do it. At last one of them took his little son by the hand and led him to the door of the King's room, and whispered to him to go and tell the King.

So the Little Boy went up to Henry and knelt down beside his chair, and crying all the time he told the dreadful tale. As Henry listened his face went white and all screwed up as if he was going to cry. Then he fell down flat on the floor in a dead faint.

When he came to, Henry was a Changed Man. He never told Funny Stories or made jokes any more and always looked Grave and Solemn. He who had been a pleasant Gentleman was now a sad and lonely Old Man, for his dear Wife was dead and so was his dear son. His daughter too was far away, for she had married the Most Important Person in Germany called the Emperor, and she had gone to Germany to live with him.

But what was to happen to England when Henry died? He thought about that, and when Matilda's husband died he wrote to her and said: "You'd better come home. England is more important than Germany and I want you to be Queen when I die."

So Matilda came home and Henry made the haughty Normans swear that they would take her for their Queen when he was dead.

However, after a bit, Matilda got tired of living a Quiet Life in England and she went and married a Gay Frenchman called Geoffrey. Henry didn't like him much and the Norman Lords just hated him. For he wasn't a Norman but a Real Frenchman, and he went about with a bit of yellow broom stuck in his hat. The Latin name for Broom is *Planta Genista*. So they called him Geoffrey Plantagenet.

As Henry grew old he became rather greedy, and one day he ate so much fish-pie that it made him dreadfully sick. So he died.

The Story of Stephen and his Cousin Matilda

By this time the Proud Normans were quite tired of being made to obey and of not being allowed to do exactly as they liked. "Look here," they said, "what about it? Henry's dead, so we needn't bother any more about having promised to take Matilda for Queen. Now there's Stephen, Henry's nephew. He's rather a softy and we could do just as we like with him. Let's make him King."

Of course that made Matilda Simply Furious. She ranted and raged round like anything. "Look here," she said, "this isn't fair.

My Father said I was to be Queen and now you go and make Stephen King. He has no *right* to be King."

But seeing that it was No Good she took her baby son, who was called Henry after his Grandfather, and ran away to Normandy. "Anyhow," she said, "if I can't be a Queen I'll be a Duchess."

But the Normans in Normandy were just as bad as the Norman Lords in England. "No," they said, "we don't want a Proud Woman for Duchess. We'll have that softy Stephen and then we can do as we like."

So Matilda and her husband had to go and live in Anjou, which was the bit of France that belonged to Geoffrey.

Then the Norman Lords in England began to do exactly as they liked. They made their servants and workmen build Strong Castles for them with great thick walls, and little slits in them for firing arrows out of. Under the castles they made fearful Dark Dungeons and dug ditches round them. They filled the ditches with water and had Bridges across them that could be pulled up when Enemies came. They made holes in the roof over the doorway too, so that if an enemy *did* get across the ditch they could pour boiling oil on to him.

And when the castles were ready the Lords gathered all their Fierce Retainers (that's what their Private Soldiers were called in those days) and went Rampaging, Plundering, and Conquering all over the Kingdom. In all England there was nothing but Misery, Misery, Misery.

And King Stephen could do nothing but wring his hands, and say, "Oh dear! Oh dear! I wish they wouldn't." If he tried to stop them they just laughed at him.

Then David, King of Scotland, heard how his niece Matilda had been treated and he got angry too. So he, with a terrible wild rabble of soldiers, marched into England, Plundering and Conquering right down as far as Yorkshire. There they met a big English Army and a dreadful battle called the Battle of the Standard was fought.

The Scots were even more fierce and wild and haughty than the Normans. But they weren't so well trained. They hadn't any armour, and instead of spears and bows and arrows like the English they had only claymores and battle-axes. So although they fought like Wild Cats they were badly beaten. Then Uncle David, feeling he'd done enough to help his niece, marched back into Scotland. But he kept a big bit of the North of England which he had Conquered. So he hadn't done so badly for himself.

Soon after this a lot of the English got tired of the terrible mess Stephen was making of things. "Even a woman would be better than this," they said. So they sent messages to Matilda and asked her to come back again.

She came, bringing a lot of Foreign Soldiers with her. Lots of the English, and even some of the Norman Lords, joined her and there was still more fighting. This is called Civil War. It isn't in the least Civil. Quite the Contrary. It is the very Worst Kind of War, because it means that brothers are fighting against brothers and Fathers against Sons, all Taking Sides.

At last Matilda and her army got shut up in Oxford and Stephen's army lay all round the Walls of the Town.

Stephen's army was so watchful that Matilda and her army couldn't get out and no food could be brought in, and Matilda and her soldiers began to starve with hunger. They were freezing with cold too, for it was a dreadfully cold winter and they had no wood to make fires with.

Matilda was getting hungrier and hungrier. "Oh, I can't stand this any longer!" she cried. "Isn't there any way of getting out of this?

"Well, we might try," said one of her faithful Knights thoughtfully, looking at the fields covered thick with snow. "If we dressed ourselves all in white they mightn't see us, or if they did they might think that we were ghosts and they'd be too frightened to come near us."

So at night the little side gate of Oxford Castle opened slowly and four figures all in white slipped quietly out and silently flitted away over the Snow. They were the Queen of England and three Faithful Followers. Soon they reached the Thames, which they easily crossed on the ice, and so got safely away.

After that Matilda ran back to France and gave up trying to be a Queen.

How Little Henry Grew Up

Meanwhile Matilda's baby son Henry had been growing up. He was now a handsome slender boy. He was good at Lessons and could remember everything he had read. He could ride and hunt and was afraid of nothing.

As the years went on and Henry heard about the dreadful state of things in England he grew very angry. "Look here, Mother, what are you going to do about it?" he would ask.

"Oh, Henry dear, what can I do?" Matilda would say. "I have tried, indeed I have, and it is No Good. They won't have me."

"Well if *you* won't do anything, *I* shall," Henry would say. "One of these days I mean to be King of England."

So when he was still little more than a School-boy he set about Doing Things and making other people do them too. And he had such a way with him that he generally got what he wanted. It is true he had a terrible temper. But his rages were soon over and then he was quite ready to shake hands and be friends again.

The first thing Henry did was to get the Haughty Normans
to let him be their Duke. Then when his father Geoffrey died
he became Count of Anjou. After that he married a Very Rich
French Princess who was Lady of all the South of France. So
before he was twenty Henry was one of the Most Important
Persons in France.

When Henry had settled Things nicely in France he gathered
a lot of Faithful Followers together and sailed over to England to
fight for his Crown.

But he hardly needed to fight at all. For in spite of all the
Killings and Ravagings of the fierce Norman Lords there were
still some Good and Great men left in England who loved Peace
and Quiet.

These men were simply horrified at the idea of a New War and so they decided to arrange a meeting between the bright-eyed determined young man and the poor old broken-down King.

This was called a Conference. Henry went to the Conference quite determined not to Give Way. But when he saw King Stephen looking so white and sad he felt sorry for him.

"Look here, Cousin," he said; "if you like I'll let you keep the Crown till you die. But you must promise to leave it to me in your Will so that I can be King without any more Bothers."

So it was arranged like that and Henry went back to France to wait. He hadn't long to wait, for in a few months Stephen died and Henry came sailing back to England, where everyone was jolly glad to see him – everyone, that is, except the Wicked Norman Lords.

Henry II. The King who was Never Idle

When Henry II first came and sat on the Throne he was only twenty-one. If there was one thing that Henry hated more than any another it was being idle. And as for lazy people he simply could not bear them. So he was soon very busy and made other people be busy too.

He was called Henry Plantagenet after his father Geoffrey who used to go about with a bit of Yellow Broom stuck in his hat. After him, for hundreds of years, all the Kings of England were called Plantagenets. It was their Family Name just as yours may be Brown or Jones or MacDonald or O'Neill.

One of the first things Henry did was to send all the strange soldiers out of England.

"Who brought all these strange soldiers here?" he asked.

"We did," said the Wicked Lords.

"Well, you can just send them away again," said Henry, "and pretty quick too."

"Oh, we can't do that," said the Wicked Lords; "we must have someone to fight our Battles."

"No, you mustn't," said Henry. "I don't like fighting at all. But if there *has* to be War *I* shall make it, not *you*. So off they go."

And off they went.

"Now," said Henry sternly, "those Castles that you have all been building, I don't like them. They are nothing but dens of Thieves and Robbers. You must pull them down."

And pulled down they were. The Dreadful Dungeons too were broken open and all the poor prisoners who had been starving there for years and years came blinking out into the sunlight again.

"What's all this queer-looking money I see about?" asked Henry.

"Well," said the Wicked Lords, "the Poor People wouldn't give us their cows and corn and things unless we paid for them. And it was tiresome *always* having to kill them to get their things, so we just made money."

"You had the Impudence," said Henry very cold and stern, "to cheat *my* poor people like that. You knew *your* money was worth nothing. It was just Sheer Robbery. Bring it all to my Mint."

So all the bad money was brought to the Royal Mint (that's where money is made) and melted down. Then Henry had Real Money made with his own picture on it so that poor people couldn't be cheated any more.

"And," said Henry, "if I find any of you Barons making money again you'll be brought before my Judges and punished."

For that was another thing Henry did. He found that in all England there were no proper Judges and that the Barons did mostly all the judging. And very badly they did it too.

"This won't do at all," said Henry. "I must have Judges whose business it is to do nothing else but Do Justice."

So he chose several Wise Men and made them go all over England settling quarrels and sending bad people to prison and all that sort of thing. This was called Going on Circuit, for each Judge went round in a circle as it were and came back to the place he had started from.

All these Things and many more Henry II did. Soon the People, from being poor and miserable, became happy and comfortable.

Henry II and Thomas à Becket

Henry had some Good Men to help him to get Things Done. But the best of them was Thomas à Becket. The King saw how clever Thomas was and he made him his Top Person, which was called Being Chancellor.

Thomas was a good deal older than King Henry, but they soon became Great Friends. They would work ever so hard together and when the work for the Day was finished they'd go off together and play about like a couple of school-boys.

Or Thomas à Becket might say, "My Lord King, you look tired and hungry. I don't believe you have had a Good Square Meal for ever so long. You'd better come to my house and have a Decent Dinner."

For Henry was dreadfully careless about his meals. He'd swallow his dinner anyhow, standing up, or walking about Doing

Things, just taking a bite when he could get it. Sitting down to a long dinner seemed to him such a Waste of Time.

He was careless about his clothes too. He'd go about in any old coat and never wear his Crown or Royal Robes unless he simply had to.

But Thomas was quite different. He soon became a Very Rich Man. He always dressed in Silk and Velvet with gold chains round his neck all glittering with jewels. He lived in a Very Grand Palace and had heaps and heaps of Nice Things to eat; indeed his dinners were so grand that all the Noble Lords wanted to come to them.

The Poor People had hated the Rich Barons who went about making a Grand Show. But they didn't hate Thomas à Becket. They loved him, for they knew that he was helping their Good King to make them happy. Henry too liked to see his Chancellor looking so grand. So everything went on Splendidly until one day Henry thought that he must make the Clergymen Live Better Lives.

Henry found that a lot of the Clergymen, like most other things in England, had gone Bad. Some of the High Up ones especially were just as bad as the Wicked Barons had been at killing people and robbing them and putting them into Dreadful Dungeons. They didn't pay any taxes either and just behaved exactly as they liked. And Henry found that he couldn't punish them. When he tried they said, "Oh no, you can't do anything to Us because we belong to the Church and everybody that belongs to the Church is Holy."

"Oh, but that's Nonsense," said Henry; "if you break the Laws you must be punished like other people."

So Henry made up his mind to change all that. And when the Archbishop of Canterbury died he said to Thomas à Becket, "I'm going to make you Archbishop and you can help me to make the Clergymen better. You learned being a Clergyman when you were young, you are the Very Best Person to help me."

"No, I'm not," said Thomas; "if you make me Archbishop we shall quarrel."

"But why?"

"Because I don't think you should go meddling with the Church. It's Holy."

"But that's just what it isn't," cried Henry. "A whole lot of Clergymen are very wicked and I want to make them Holy so that they can be an example to my Poor People."

And so Henry, who liked having his Own Way, made Thomas Archbishop. Then what Thomas said would happen happened. They quarrelled. They went on quarrelling.

Thomas became a Changed Man. He left off wearing fine silks and velvets and golden chains and jewels and wore ugly clothes and a scratchy shirt next to his skin. He left off eating nice food and just had bread and water and perhaps a bit of cheese or an egg, and was just as aggravating as he could be.

Then one day when Thomas had been more aggravating than ever, Henry got into a Furious Temper. "Are there none of you Lazy Good-for-Nothing Knights who will rid me of this Botheration Priest?" he shouted, stamping his foot with Rage.

Henry didn't mean it. He was just in a Temper, and people often say things they Don't Mean when they get into Tempers.

However, some of his Knights heard what he said. They didn't like being called Lazy Good-for-Nothings and they just thought they'd show the King that they could be as busy as anyone else. So they went off as fast as they could to Canterbury and killed Thomas in his Very Own Cathedral.

When the people heard about it they were as sorry as could be and cried and cried because they had lost their "dear Archbishop." They were angry too – angry with their Good King because they thought that he had told the Wicked Knights to kill Thomas. But Henry was really sorrier than anyone else and he made up his mind to punish himself for having lost his Temper and saying those Wicked Words. So he took off all his clothes except his shorts and walked to Canterbury on his bare feet with a lighted candle in his hand. When he came to the place where Thomas was buried he fell on his knees. And there he stayed praying all day long and all through the dark night with nothing to eat or drink. Then in the morning he made the priests give him a good Thrashing on his bare back. And after that he felt better. But although Henry could punish himself, he couldn't bring his Dear Friend back again.

But the Pope made Thomas into a Saint. So he is called Saint Thomas à Becket.

How Henry II became Lord of Ireland

When Henry II was King of England, Ireland was all divided up into bits as England had been in the Saxon days. There were five or six Kings generally, and they spent a lot of time quarrelling about who was Top King.

Now Henry was Very Rich. "It would be quite easy," he said to himself, "to go Conquering in Ireland. I could just knock down one King after another like a row of ninepins. Then I'd be Top King over the Irish and stop them quarrelling about it."

So he asked the Pope, "Can I go Conquering in Ireland?"

Just then the Pope was rather angry with some of the Irish Kings. So he said, "Why yes, you can. That's a Very Good Idea."

Then two of the Irish Kings had a Dreadful quarrel and King O'Ruarc chased King Dermot out of his Kingdom. Dermot had heard what a Great Ruler Henry was so he went to him and said, "Oh, please help me to get back My Kingdom and I'll make you my Top King."

"Yes," said Henry, "I'd like that, but I'm too Busy just now. However, I daresay, if you asked them, some of my Good Barons would help you."

So Dermot went to some of the Barons and asked them.

And they said, "Thank you very much, we'd like to." So they gathered their Retainers and Faithful Followers and went off to Ireland. There they went rampaging about, conquering some of the Kings and frightening the rest. Then Henry thought he'd go and see what they were doing. When he got to Ireland the People seemed quite pleased to see him. So he just travelled about in all the five or six Kingdoms and said, "Now I'm your Top King, and you must obey me."

And the Kings said, "Yes, we will take you as our Top King."

Then Henry went home thinking he had Conquered Ireland. But of course he hadn't. It was just the beginning of Lots of Bothers with Ireland. But after that he called himself "Lord of Ireland" as well as all the other grand names he had already.

Henry was a Great King and ruled England well. But his sons were always being disobedient and causing him Great Grief. However, they all died except Richard and John.

Although Richard was always rebelling he wasn't a Bad Man; not Going-to-Prison Bad. John was Bad. He was a mean little Sneak. But he never rebelled against his Father because he thought he'd get more out of him if he pretended to be good and obedient. And Henry loved John more than any of his other children.

At last Henry got very ill, and as he was lying there in bed, being very ill, someone came and told him, "Your son John has started Rebelling against you."

Poor Henry just couldn't bear it, "Oh, John, John!" he cried. "Now I don't want to live any longer."

So he died.

Richard I. The Lion-Heart

Richard had been out Rebelling against his Father when, returning Home one day, he met a Grand Funeral. It was so splendid that he asked, "Whose Grand Funeral is that?"

"It is the Great King of England's," he was told.

"Oh, I'm sorry," said Richard. "I'm sorry." Then he covered his face with his hands and cried and cried. He wished that he had been a better son. Now it was too late.

But Richard was not the sort of Person to be Sorry for long. So he soon Cheered Up and went and had himself crowned.

He was not the sort of Person either to like staying at Home and Ruling well, and Thinking of the Good-of-his-People. What he liked best was going Fighting and having Exciting Adventures. In fact, he didn't like the English People much at all. For nearly all his life he'd lived in France and could hardly talk English.

His Greatest Friend was Philip, King of France. But Philip wasn't a True Friend and didn't really love Richard. He just egged him on to rebel against his Father. "For," he said to himself, "if I get Richard to do the fighting for me I can easily get hold of all Henry's land in France."

Richard told two Bishops to come to see him. "Look here," he said, "I can't be Bothered with this dull old England and I'm going to The Holy Land with my Friend the King of France. We're going to fight for the Cross. You two can look after England while I'm away."

At this time The Holy Land belonged to people called Saracens. They weren't Christians and they didn't take any Care of The Holy Places where Our Lord was Born and Lived and Died. So every Now and Again the Christian Kings and Princes gathered armies together and went to fight the Saracens and try

to get Jerusalem and the Holy Places away from them. These
Wars were called Crusades, or Wars of the Cross. And it was
thought a Very Fine Thing to go on one.

So our King Richard and the King of France went off to do a
War of the Cross. Richard was just terribly brave. He loved doing
Fights and Daring Deeds. He was better at it than anyone else so
he was called the Lion-Heart.

The Fact was that as Richard was always best at doing Daring
Deeds, he got all the Praise and no one paid any attention to
Philip. So he was just as jealous as jealous could be. At last he
couldn't stand being Second Best any longer and he sneaked off
home. "I'll get even with that Big Bully of an Englishman one of
these days," he grumbled to himself. And as soon as he got Home
he began Plotting with Richard's Bad Brother John.

For while Richard had been doing Brave Deeds in The Holy
Land things had been getting into a Pretty Fine Mess in England.

One of the Bishops whom Richard had told to rule while he was away was a Norman. He was so hard and cruel that the people wanted to rebel. So John said to them, "Yes, I would rebel if I were you. I'll help you to get rid of this cruel Priest."

John said that because he wanted to make himself King before Richard came back.

So the people rebelled. Then they wished that they hadn't, for John was far worse to them than the Bishops had been. Then the King of France came and said, "Look here, John, you help me and we'll go conquering all Richard's French Lands. Then we can share them between us." So the two of them went Conquering.

At last, far away in The Holy Land, Richard heard of all these wicked Betrayings and he thought that he had better come home and do something about it. So he started off, but on the way his ship got wrecked and nearly all the soldiers and people were drowned. Then the Duke of Austria got hold of him and put him in Prison. For Richard and the Duke had quarrelled in The Holy Land, and the Duke hated him.

However, when the Emperor of Germany heard about it, he wrote to the Duke and said, "I want the King of England. Send him to me."

"Shan't," said the Duke; "not unless you pay me a lot of money."

"All right," said the Emperor.

So he paid the Duke a lot of money, and then he put Richard in Prison.

When Philip heard that Richard was in Prison he was just as glad as he could be.

John was glad too, for he could go on doing what he liked, plundering and robbing the wretched English People.

And poor Richard could do nothing but sit in prison and be

sad, and write Sad Poetry. Then when the English People heard that their King was shut up in Prison they were sad too. For they loved their King although they hardly knew him. They were proud that he was so Brave and able to fight better than anyone else so that everyone was afraid of him. And they wanted him to come home and stop John from being so wicked.

So they sent to the Emperor and asked him, "Please let Richard go free."

"Oh no," said the Emperor; "I've promised the King of France to keep him safe."

"But we will give you a lot of money for him," said the English.

"All right," said the Emperor. "You can have him. But send me the money first."

Now bad John had robbed the English People of such a lot of money that they hadn't much left. But they scraped and saved until they had got enough. Then they sent it to the Emperor and he set Richard free.

As soon as he got out of Prison Richard hurried home. And John, who was a coward as well as everything else that was Bad, soon came sneaking up to him saying he hadn't meant any harm and asking to be forgiven.

Richard forgave John but he couldn't forgive Philip, and as soon as he had settled things in England he went off to France to fight him. He was still fighting there when he was hit by an arrow and wounded so badly that he died.

John Lackland

John was called Lackland because when his father Henry II died he hadn't left him any Lands to rule over. Henry had loved John best of all his sons. But in spite of that he knew that he wouldn't be a good Ruler. So he didn't leave him any land.

But as soon as Richard was dead John went and made himself King of England. He hadn't any right to do that. The Proper Person to be the next King was John's Nephew, Prince Arthur. But Arthur was only a boy. "Boys don't need Crowns and Thrones and Things," John said to himself. So he got hold of Arthur and put him in Prison. Then he thought, "What is the Good of That? Arthur will soon Grow Up. Then people will begin Rebelling and saying he ought to be King. That will just make a Whole Lot of Bother. I'd better Kill him." So he killed him.

That was the kind of Wicked Uncle John was.

As long as Richard was alive, John and Philip King of France had been as thick as Thieves. But now they quarrelled, for all Philip had wanted was to get hold of the English King's lands in France.

Philip now said that John had no Right to be King and that Prince Arthur was the Proper Person. And when he heard that John had killed Arthur he got into a Furious Temper.

So now Philip began a War with John and went Conquering in his French Lands. And John just sat still and let him carry on how he liked. He stayed safely in his Castle eating and drinking and amusing himself and bragging about the Great Deeds he could do if he liked.

When at last he heard that Philip was coming against the Castle where he was idling he got frightened and ran away back to England. So nearly all the Broad Lands in France that Henry II had owned were lost.

But really this was a Good Thing, for now brave Englishmen hadn't to go and get Killed in France just because the English King wanted to call himself Duke of Normandy, Count of Anjou, and goodness else knows what besides.

Soon after this John began a Fierce Quarrel with the Pope, who, you remember, was Top Person over all the Churches in the World.

John made a new Archbishop, but the Pope said, "No, you can't do that. I make Archbishops, not you."

So he sent a man called Stephen Langton to be Archbishop. But John wouldn't have him and chased him out of the country.

Now the Pope had a habit of taking away Crowns and Thrones from Kings who wouldn't obey him, so he told John, "You are no longer King of England. No one need obey you. Anyone who likes can kill you."

Still John would not Give In. Then the Pope said to the King of France, "John is being very disobedient; you can go and Conquer England and take his Crown from him. It would be a Good Deed."

"Thank you very much," said the King of France; "I should like nothing better." So he began to gather his army together to go and Conquer England.

Then all of a sudden John got frightened. In a frantic hurry he wrote a letter to the Pope. "Please," he said, "I'm very sorry. I'll do anything you tell me."

"Ah!" said the Pope; "he's sorry is he? Well, he can't get off with just saying he's sorry. He's got to be taught a lesson."

So he called one of his Important People and told him, "Go to England and take away John's crown and keep it till he promises to take me as Top Person over him and to pay me a lot of money every year."

The Pope's Important Person set off for England, and when he came to the King's Palace John got off his Throne, knelt down before him, and taking his Crown from his head gave it to the Important Person.

The Important Person kept the Crown for five days and before he gave it back John had to promise to obey the Pope in everything and say that he was only King of England because the Pope allowed him, that in fact he was only the Pope's servant. This was called Doing Homage.

A Day to Remember

The people of England were angry when they heard what the King had done. But soon they had reason to be still more angry. For now that he was friends again with the Pope John behaved worse than ever. He robbed people, put them in prison, and cut off their heads like anything.

At last the People couldn't bear it any longer, so they said to the Barons (who were now Noble English Gentlemen), "We really can't stand this misery any more. Won't you do something?"

The Barons got together and talked.

"Suppose," said one of them, "that we made a List of all the Things he must do and all the Things he mustn't do. Then we could take it to him and make him Seal it with the Great Seal and make it a Law. Perhaps that would make him behave better."

So they made a List and in it they put things like:

You are not to put anyone in prison unless he has done something wrong.

Even if he has really done something wrong you are not to put him in prison until you have taken him to a Just Judge and had him Judged.

You are not to take away a Farmer's Ploughs and Carts and Things that he needs for farming.

You are not to take away a workman's hammer or chisel or anything he needs to do his work with.

There were lots more things in the List, so they called it the Great Writing, or Magna Carta.

John was Simply Furious at the Idea that anyone should try to stop him doing exactly as he liked. But the Barons determined to make him. They put on their shining armour and with their swords in their hands they went to meet John at a place called Runnymede on the Thames.

By this time John had hardly any friends left, and when he saw all these stern Barons with swords in their hands he got frightened. So he promised to keep all the rules the Barons had made and he sealed Magna Carta, and it became the Law.

This was on the 15th June. It was a Great Day for England. For this Magna Carta was the true beginning of our Freedom.

Very soon the Barons found that it wasn't much good making John promise things, for he broke all the rules and behaved worse than ever. So they got together again and talked. "We can't put up with this any longer," they said. "We must fight."

"We must drive him off the Throne."

"Then who'll we have for King?"

"Why not send to France and ask Prince Louis to come and be King?"

"What a Good Idea. We'll do that."

Of course Louis was as pleased as anything at the Idea of being King of England. So he quickly gathered his Faithful Followers and came sailing over the sea from France.

But he had his trouble for nothing, for one day John went out and got soaking wet. He didn't change his clothes when he came in, so he got an Awful Cold. Then he made himself so sick with eating a lot of peaches that he died.

As soon as John was dead the Barons went to Louis.

"Thank you very much," they said, "for so kindly coming to help us. But we don't need you any more. You see, John's dead and that changes everything. His son Henry is a nice little boy so we're going to make him King and you can go home to France now."

"Indeed I won't!" shouted Louis in a rage. "You asked me to come and be King and I'm going to stay."

"Oh, well, if you won't go quietly," said the Barons, "we'll have to fight you."

And they did. They beat Louis so badly that in the end he was glad to get out of the country.

Henry III. The King who Broke his Promises

As Henry III was only nine when he became King he couldn't of course do the Ruling. So wise men ruled for him. They did their best to clear up the mess John had left and tried to make People Happy and Comfortable again.

Henry III was a kind gentle little boy and Good at his Lessons. But unfortunately he *would* tell lies. You couldn't believe a word he said and he always broke his Promises. So in spite of the wise Teachers he had he didn't grow up into a Nice Man.

He was always shilly-shallying and always having Favourites. He spent far too much money, mostly in silly little wars that did nobody any good. Some, it is true, he spent in better ways, such as building beautiful Churches like Westminster Abbey. But mostly he just wasted it.

Henry broke the rules of Magna Carta Over and Over again. And as he was always asking the Barons to give him More and More Money, they used to tell him that he couldn't have it unless he promised to Keep the Rules.

That really wasn't Much Good, for Henry never minded promising anything, because he never meant to keep his promises.

Henry really liked the French better than he did the English, and he married a French Lady called Eleanor. She brought a whole lot of French people with her, and Henry just loved them. He petted them like anything, gave them all the best places, and let them break the Laws as much as they liked. This made the English Barons Very Angry.

After a bit a Nobleman called Simon de Montfort made himself Top Person among the Barons. At first they didn't like him because of his name, which is French.

"Here's another Frenchman," they said, "come to rob us."

But they were wrong, for although Simon had a French name he loved England. And the English soon came to like him very much and do as he told them. At first Henry too loved him and seemed as if he couldn't make enough of him. But when he found that Simon wanted to make him rule properly Henry began to hate him, and at last they fought. Simon got the best of it, and he put Henry in Prison and did the Ruling all by himself for a time.

It was while Simon was doing the Ruling that he hit upon a Grand Idea.

Of course with such a troublesome King the Barons had often to meet and Talk Things over. Then they had to go and talk to the King wherever he might be. Sometimes they had to trail half over England to find him. That was very tiresome and wasted a lot of time.

So one day Simon said, "This won't do at all. We must have somewhere that we can go to at certain times every year and Talk about the Things that are wrong in the Country. The King must come too. We won't only have Barons and Bishops, we'll have two Gentlemen from every County and two Ordinary People from each of the big Towns. Then everyone can tell about his own County or his own Town."

They called the Talking Place the Parliament because *parler* means 'to Talk' in French.

Henry III was King for fifty-six years and in all that long time the beginning of Parliament is the only truly Worth While Thing to remember.

Edward I. The Lawgiver

When Henry III died the Barons met together and looked at each other, wondering what to do. For Henry's son Edward was not in England. He was far away in The Holy Land doing a War of the Cross.

So what were the Barons to do? There was the Throne empty and the Crown waiting, but no King.

"This is what we must do," said one of the Barons; "we must swear here and now to be true to our King. Then when he comes Home he will know that we are indeed his Faithful Followers."

And it shows how much the People loved Peace and Quiet that they did so keep the Peace. No one rebelled; no one tried to trump up another King. They just waited.

Then one August day the King's great Ship came sailing into Dover harbour. Edward I had come home.

The People seemed to go mad with joy. They cheered him all the way to London, where he was Crowned. The people sang and danced and feasted. All the fountains in London spouted out wine instead of water. Oxen were roasted whole in the streets; baskets full of cakes and pies stood about so that everyone could eat and drink as much as he liked.

Then when all the Parties were over Edward took off his Crown and Royal Robes and settled down to work and see what he could do to make his People Happy and Comfortable.

For Edward loved England and the English. He felt that they were his own People and that he must take care of them.

So he kept all the rules of Magna Carta and he made a lot more good laws. In fact, he made so many good laws that they called him the Lawgiver.

The people gave him another nickname too. They called him Longshanks because he had such long legs. That shows they liked him, because usually we give nicknames only to people we like very much.

But you mustn't think that Edward was just a tall Angel! For he wasn't. He could be Perfectly Horrid to people he didn't like and was Very Very cruel to his enemies. He was Rather Interfering too. If he wanted a thing badly he just took it even if he had No Right to it.

Edward I and the First English Prince of Wales

When Edward had settled things nicely in England he began to think that he would like to rule over the whole Island. "Why shouldn't I rule over Wales and Scotland as well as England?" he said to himself. "It really would be far better just to have one King instead of having a Prince ruling in Wales and another King ruling in Scotland. These Welsh now – we are always having Bothers with them and if I were King of Wales I'd soon stop all that. They'd have to obey me and I'd do the Ruling far better than that Prince they have now."

Edward called a messenger and told him, "Go to the Prince of Wales and tell him to come and Do Homage to me."

The messenger went to the Prince of Wales and said, "King Edward says that you are to go and Do Homage to him."

"Why?" asked the Prince.

"Because he says you are."

"Well, you can go back and tell him that I'm not coming. He isn't my Top King and he has no Right over Wales or over me."

Again and again Edward sent and each time the messenger came back with the same answer, and each time Edward got crosser and crosser.

Then Edward heard that a beautiful Lady who was his own Cousin was coming from France and going to be married to the Prince of Wales.

So he called one of his Captains. "Take a fast ship," he said, "and go to meet the ship which is carrying the Lady Eleanor to Wales. Bring the Lady here. Tell her that she must be married from my Palace of Westminster."

Lady Eleanor, instead of going on to Wales, was taken to London. She was treated kindly, but all the same she was a prisoner.

Then Edward wrote a letter to the Prince of Wales. "The Lady Eleanor is here," he said. "When you come to Do Homage you shall be married to her."

The poor Prince hardly knew what to do for grief and rage. He called Edward all the Bad Names he could think of. Not even to gain his dear Lady would he kneel to Edward and swear to obey him. He wouldn't kneel, but he would fight for his Lady.

So he gathered his Faithful Followers together. Edward too gathered his and in a Furious Temper Marched into Wales. Edward was a very good soldier. He had far more men than the Prince of Wales, so the Welsh were beaten and their Prince taken prisoner. Then at last he had to bend his proud knees and Do Homage to Edward.

As soon as he had got what he wanted Edward became quite pleasant. He made a splendid wedding for the Prince and Princess and gave them lots and lots of presents, and sent them home to Wales.

So for a time there was peace. But not for long. The Prince of Wales just couldn't stand Edward's interfering ways, so he began Rebelling. Once more Edward marched into Wales and this time he fought so fiercely that the Welsh got dreadfully badly beaten. Their Prince and nearly all the Most Important People got killed.

So very sadly the Welsh Barons went to King Edward and knelt before him and took him as their King.

And having got what he wanted Edward was quite pleasant again. "Don't look so sad and sorry," he said. "I promise to give you a Prince born in Wales who can't speak either French or English. In a few days I'll bring him to you."

When the day came all the Most Important Persons gathered together. And when they were all there Edward came to them carrying a Baby in his arms.

"Here is your Prince," he said. "He is my little Son. He was born here in Wales only a few days ago. And as I told you, he can't speak either French or English."

So England and Wales became joined together, and since then the eldest son of the King of England has always been chosen as Prince of Wales.

Edward I. The Hammer of the Scots

After he'd got Wales, Edward became more eager than ever to get Scotland too and it wasn't very long before he got his chance.

The King of Scotland died and his little granddaughter became Queen. But she was living in Norway with her Father, and on her way home to be Crowned she died. So there was neither a King nor a Queen in Scotland and ever so many of the Most Important Persons began quarrelling about who should be King.

At last someone said, "Look here. Let's ask somebody to settle this for us."

"What about King Edward?" said someone. "He's good at Laws and that sort of thing. He ought to know."

So they sent to King Edward and asked him, "Please will you tell us which of us ought to be King."

"Ha, ha!" said Edward to himself. "Now's my chance!" And he pretended that he had been asked to decide who should be King because he was Top King over Scotland.

So he thought about it and looked up old books, and then he said, "John Baliol should be King."

And all the other Important Persons said, "All right; we'll have John Baliol."

Then Edward got John quietly by himself. "Now, John," he said, "I've made you King, so you must Do Homage to me and take me for Top King."

John hadn't bargained for that and he didn't like the idea. But he was a poor weak thing and very pleased at the idea of being a King. "If I don't do what Edward asks me," he said to himself, "perhaps he won't let me be King. Anyhow I don't suppose this Homage business means anything very much."

So he Did Homage.

Of course the Scottish people were very much annoyed when they heard what John had done. But they too thought, "Well, perhaps it doesn't mean much."

But very soon they found out that it meant a lot. For Edward began interfering in all sorts of ways. The Scots wouldn't stand that. So they rebelled.

Then Edward marched into Scotland with a great army, Fighting and Rampaging right up to Aberdeen. Then he went to Scone and took away the Stone of Destiny on which the Scottish Kings sat when they were crowned. It was supposed to be the stone which Jacob used as a pillow when he slept in the desert and saw angels climbing up a ladder into Heaven. It was said that wherever it was, there Scottish Kings would be crowned. So Edward took it away and put it in Westminster Abbey.

Edward marched back to England with his spoils thinking he had conquered Scotland. But of course he hadn't. It was just the beginning of a lot of Bothers and useless fighting. More than anything he wanted to conquer Scotland, and he couldn't do it, although to the end of his life he kept trying.

He was on his way to Scotland to have another try when he became very ill. He felt he was going to die. So he called his son Edward Prince of Wales to him.

"Edward," said the King, "all these years I've hammered and hammered away at Scotland and I haven't conquered it yet. Promise me that you will never, never stop fighting these Scots until you've beaten them and made yourself King of Scotland."

"Oh yes, Father, of course," said Edward. "Don't you worry."

So King Edward died and Scotland still remained unconquered.

Edward II. Scotland Still Remains Free

Edward II was a lazy Good-for-Nothing Kind of King. So now he said, "Why should I bother about this Old War? I won't."

Of course giving up a silly war like trying to Conquer Scotland was quite a Good Idea if Edward had only done it properly. But he didn't. He left a whole lot of soldiers in Scotland.

By this time the Scots had got a Very Good King called Robert the Bruce. He made up his mind to drive all the English soldiers out of Scotland. He fought so well that he got back all the towns the English had taken except Stirling.

When Edward heard about Stirling being the very last town the English had got left, he said, "Oh, well, perhaps I'd better go and help them."

So he gathered the most splendid army ever was seen. It was all full of Barons and Knights in shining Armour. And away he marched up to Scotland with banners waving and trumpets blowing, making ever such a Grand Show.

But when the two armies met at Bannockburn, near Stirling, it was the great English army that got beaten. Ever so many got killed and ever so many ran away. And when Edward saw that, he too got on his horse and rode away as fast as he could. Away and away he galloped until he got safely back to England.

That was the end of all Edward I's Conquerings in Scotland. And Scotland was still Free.

After this things got worse and worse in England. The Barons got more and more tired of Edward and Kept on Rebelling. At last they couldn't stand it any longer. So they put Edward in Prison and made his little son, who was also called Edward, King instead.

And in Prison poor miserable King Edward II died.

Edward III. The Knights of the Garter

Edward III was fourteen when the Barons put the Crown on his head, and told him that he was King of England.

"Am I to rule now?" asked Edward.

"Certainly not," said his Mother, Queen Isabella, who had been a French Princess. "You attend to your lessons. I am going to do the Ruling."

Now Queen Isabella was a Very Bad Lady and her Favourite was a Bad Baron called Mortimer. Between the two of them they did a whole lot of Wicked Deeds and the poor People had a Very Unhappy time.

Edward was a clever boy; he was pretty good at lessons, but what he liked best was to listen to stories of the Great Deeds of his Grandfather, Edward I, or of Richard the Lion-Heart. But perhaps best of all he liked the Stories of Arthur, the Very Special British King.

And thinking of all these Grand Times, Edward wished that he could grow up quickly so that he could Do Things. It didn't take him long to see that everything was going All Wrong in England. For the Bad Baron Mortimer grew worse and worse with his Killings and Betrayings and everyone just hated him.

So Edward made friends with some Good Barons, and when he was about eighteen he told them, "All these Killings and Betrayings have got to stop. We must get hold of that Bad Baron and Kill *him*."

But it wasn't easy to get hold of him, for by day he went about with his Fierce Retainers, at night he locked the door of his strong Castle and the Queen put the key under her pillow.

At last, however, Edward's Faithful Followers found a Secret Passage into the Castle and one dark night they got in and seized the Bad Baron in his Bed.

"Now," said Edward, "you are going to be tried for all your Wicked Deeds. You'll probably be hanged."

And hanged he was.

Edward began to do the Ruling and soon Things got better. And when Things had settled down a bit Edward made his Round Table and had his Best Knights to dinner. He gave balls too, and one day at a ball a Lady's garter came off. Some of the Knights began to giggle rudely, which made the King Very Angry.

"I'm ashamed of you," he said, "laughing like that at a Lady," and he went and picked up the garter and politely gave it back to her.

"I'm ashamed of you," he said again to the Knights, "I'm going to make some new Knights and I'll call them The Knights of the Garter. They will be the Very Best Knights, and a Garter will be the best prize that I can give to anyone.

So the King had some beautiful garters made all of gold and precious stones and gave them to his best Knights. And ever since then when the King wants to do Great Honour to anyone he makes him a Garter Knight.

The Prince of Wales gets his Crest and Motto

Things seemed to be going on very nicely when Edward took it into his head that he would like to be King of France.

"My mother was the last French King's sister, so I don't see why I shouldn't be King of France. I'm his nephew and I've a better right to the Throne than the King they have chosen. He's only a cousin."

So he sent to the French and told them, "I'm coming to be your next King."

"Oh no, thank you," said the French; "we don't want you. We'd much rather have the King we've chosen."

"Well," said Edward, "I'm going to call myself King of France, and if you don't let me be it I'll fight you for it."

So Edward began a War with France. It was called The Hundred Years War, because for a hundred years the Kings of England went on fighting to make themselves Kings of France. Of course they didn't go on fighting every day for a Hundred Years, but they fought a terrible lot.

One of the Battles was called The Battle of Crécy. King Edward didn't do any fighting in it because he wanted his Son, Edward Prince of Wales, to show how Brave he was.

The Prince of Wales was just Seventeen, and he was called the Black Prince because he always wore black armour.

At Crécy Edward climbed up into a Windmill and sat there looking on out of a high-up window while the Black Prince did the fighting. But there were such a dreadful lot of French soldiers that some of the Most Important people thought that the Black Prince was sure to get killed.

But the Prince was so Brave that he won the Battle.

And when the King saw that the Battle was won he hurried down from the Windmill as fast as he could and threw his arms round the Prince of Wales and kissed him before all the soldiers.

"Oh, my dear Boy," he cried, "I am proud of you. Now I can make you a Knight."

For although anyone could be Born a Prince he couldn't be a Knight until he had done Something Big and Fine. And now Edward made him not just an ordinary Knight but a Top one, a Knight of the Garter, and gave him a pair of gold spurs.

Being given a pair of Gold Spurs was one of the prizes for being made a Knight. So when anyone did something very Daring and Dashing people used to say, "Oh, he has won his spurs."

"And now, my boy, you can have something painted on your Shield," said King Edward when he'd made the Black Prince a Knight.

For before Barons and Nobles had done any Great Deeds they just had plain shields. After they had done Something Worth While they had things painted on them.

"Thank you, Father, I've chosen already," said the Prince. "I'm going to have Three Ostrich Feathers and my Motto is going to be *Ich Dien* which means 'I Serve.'"

"A very good Motto too," said the King, "for of course a good Prince must do everything he can to Serve his People. But how did you think of it?"

"I didn't think of it. I found it."

"Found it! Where?"

"In the Battle," said the Prince. "It belonged to the King of Bohemia. But he went and got himself killed, poor man. So I can take his Crest and Motto."

And ever since then the Prince of Wales has had Three Feathers for his Crest and "I Serve" has been his Motto.

Edward III gets Thirty Thousand Sacks of Wool

Edward went on and on with his Conquering in France. But it didn't seem to make a bit of difference and Edward was no nearer being King of France than he had been. And he spent far too much money. For War always costs a terrible lot. So Edward was always asking for more and more money.

Once when Edward asked for money Parliament said, "No, really we can't give you any money this time. But we'll give you thirty thousand Sacks of Wool." Wool was the thing English Merchants made most of their money out of.

So that made Edward think about Wool, and what it was best to do with it so as to make money out of it for his Wars. And he found out that although English wool was the Best, English Weavers didn't know how to weave it into fine cloth. For their grand cloths they used to send their wool to Flanders to get it woven. "Well now," said Edward, "wouldn't it be better if we could weave our own wool in our own Country?" So he brought some Flemish Weavers over from France to teach the English. And in this way it was really Edward III who began making England into a Manufacturing Country. And because he helped the people to find out the best ways of selling their wool to foreign Countries he was called the Father of English Commerce.

Edward also put some sacks of wool into the Parliament House for the Top Barons to sit on. "If they have to sit on Woolsacks," he said, "it will help them to remember what a Very Important thing Wool is." There is still one Woolsack in the House of Lords and The Lord Chancellor sits on it.

But although Edward helped the trade of the country he spent so much money on fighting that the people began to get poorer and poorer. So they began to hate Edward instead of loving him as they had done at first.

The Black Prince too was always going Conquering here and there and everywhere. Then with always fighting and living a Hard Life in Camps and being out in All Weathers the Black Prince just ruined his Health. So he died.

That was a Great Grief to Edward, for he had loved the Black Prince very much. He was an old man now, for he had ruled England for fifty years. He was sad too, for he knew the people didn't love him any more. And he was tired – tired of War, tired even of his grand balls and parties, so he died too.

Richard II. The Story of Wat Tyler

The next King was the Son of the Black Prince. He was only eleven when his Grandfather, Edward III, died, so of course he couldn't do the Ruling. His Uncles did that. All his Uncles were Dukes. And these Royal Dukes were the haughtiest and most Unruly of all the Barons.

They didn't care about teaching the little King how to rule. They didn't care about the Kingdom. They didn't care about the Good-of-the-People. All they cared about was making themselves Rich and Powerful.

The two Top Ones of these Wicked Uncles were called John of Gaunt, Duke of Lancaster, and Thomas, Duke of Gloucester, and they spent a lot of their time being jealous of each other. But it was John of Gaunt who ruled most. He went on Conquering in France. So he spent a lot of Money and was always having to make new taxes to get more. Edward III had to do that too, and when everything he could think of had been taxed and it was difficult to find anything new he thought of taxing people's Heads. "Everyone has a head," he said, "so I should make a lot of money." This tax was called the Poll Tax, Poll meaning Head.

Now Uncle John just couldn't think of anything new, so he said, "I'll make the Poll Tax five times bigger than it used to be." Of course the poor people didn't like that at all. "If they would tax our teeth," they said, "we'd pull them out rather than give all this money for those wretched Wars. But if we want to live at all we've got to keep our heads on our shoulders."

In those days men called Tax Collectors used to call at every House or Cottage and get the Money. And very often they were rude men with Bad Manners who got angry if they were kept waiting and didn't get the Money At Once.

One day a Tax Collector was Very Rude, and a man called Wat hit him on the head with his hammer. Wat hit so hard that the Tax Collector was killed dead.

Wat used to tile houses. So he was called Wat the Tyler. In those days lots of men got their Surnames for the things they did. Giles the Farmer became Giles Farmer, John the Baker became John Baker, and so on.

Now when Wat the Tyler's friends heard what he had done they all gathered round him, clapping him on the back and calling him a hero. But they were a little frightened too in case soldiers should come and take Wat off to prison. Then someone said, "Come on, let's go to London to see the King. If we can only talk to him he'll put everything right."

"That's a Good Idea," said the others. "Come on. Let's go."

"But we'd better have something to fight with in case the soldiers come at us," said someone else.

But they hadn't any swords and spears, so they just took their spades and axes and hammers. Then off they started to London.

On the way they passed through lots of villages and the people came running out of their houses to see what all the noise was about.

"Wat the Tyler has killed a Tax Collector," they were told, "and we're going to London to see the King. Come on with us."

So lots more men joined the crowd till there were hundreds and hundreds all Marching to London to see the King. When the great Crowd of them got as far as Blackheath they stopped there and sent a Message to the King who was living in the Tower of London.

"Please, King," they said, "will you come to speak to us? You needn't be afraid. We wouldn't hurt you for anything. But we have lots of things to tell you."

Richard told the Messenger, "Yes, I'll come to you tomorrow. You're at Blackheath, are you? Well, tell your Top People to come down to the river near Greenwich and I'll come to talk to them there."

When the others heard The News they cheered and sang and danced and made ever such a noise, although they were all very tired. And when it grew dark they lay down on the heath just as they were and went to sleep. It was a warm June night so they weren't very cold, but oh! they were hungry. And when they woke in the morning they were more hungry still. And there was nothing for breakfast.

However, they forgot about that when they saw the King's boat being rowed along the River. They got so excited that they all rushed down to the banks, pushing and shoving each other to try and get the best places for seeing.

So King Richard stood up in his boat and shouted with as loud a voice as ever he could,

"What is it you want? I've come to listen to you!"

Then all the men on the bank began shouting and yelling at once, making such a noise that you couldn't hear what they said. So after rowing up and down for a bit and not being able to understand a single word that was said the King went back home.

When the Crowd saw that the King was going away they just seemed to go mad.

"Come on," they cried, "come on. They're taking the King away. They won't let him talk to us. We'll show them."

Then they started running helter-skelter along the river banks and through the fields. On and on and on they ran till they came to shops and houses.

The shop people shut the shops and put up their shutters. But it wasn't any use. The crowd broke into all the shops of the Bakers and Grocers and just ate and drank as much as they wanted.

Then they marched down the Strand to the Duke of Gaunt's beautiful Palace called the Savoy. There they smashed up all the lovely furniture and burned the Palace to the ground. That was just to show John of Gaunt how much they hated him.

But the King was shocked at all these Goings-On. "I'm King," he said, "and really I can't allow it. Something must be done."

So after a lot of talk he got a Trusty Friend to go and tell the Men, "If you will only not be so unruly the King will come and talk to you tomorrow at Mile End."

Mile End is now a bit of London full of houses. Then it was just empty fields.

So next morning a whole lot of the men went tramping across

London Bridge. They were much quieter now. "Would the King be angry with them?" they wondered.

But when the King came riding up on his big horse they saw he didn't look angry.

"Well, my men," he said, quite quietly and kindly. "Tell me. What is it you want to say to me? And please don't all speak at once. For if you do I can't hear what you say."

"Please, King," they said, "we want to be free and not just like slaves any more."

In those days Workmen weren't free to go about from place to place to look for work. They belonged to the place where they were born and they were never allowed to leave that place. If they were born on a Farm they had to stay there always. If the Farmer was a bad Master or if he didn't pay proper wages they still had to stay. The workers were really slaves. They were called Churls and Villeins. Villein didn't mean Bad Man. It just meant Servant belonging to a Farmer. They were all tired of that sort of thing, so now they asked, "Please, King, make us free men."

"All right," said Richard. "Now go home quietly and don't let me hear of any more Rioting and Goings-On like yesterday. I'll send you letters saying that you are all to be Free Men."

Then the men set up a Great Cheer for the King and went off home. Richard too went back to the Tower of London. Then he got a whole lot of people who could write and made them sit up all night writing letters to say that all these men were to be Free.

But Wat the Tyler hadn't been among the men at Mile End and he wouldn't go home, and a whole lot of his Best Friends wouldn't go either, for they wanted the King to promise ever so many more Things. The next day they were all gathered together when Richard came riding by with a lot of Barons and Knights.

"Here's the King," said Wat, "I'm going to speak to him. But the rest of you are to stay where you are until I wave my hand. Then you must rush at these Barons and Knights and kill them all. But be sure you don't hurt the King. He's only a boy. We can soon make him do anything we like."

"King," said Wat when he got close up to him, "do you see all those men?"

"Of course I do," said Richard. "What about it?"

"Well, they're all under me. They'll do anything I tell them."

"I'm sure I don't mind," said Richard, very calmly and quietly, for he saw that Wat was in a Very Bad Temper and he didn't want to quarrel with him.

But seeing the King wasn't going to quarrel made Wat more angry than ever. And he began to be so rude that the Lord Mayor of London, who was beside the King, lost *his* temper.

"That's not the way to speak to the King," he said to Wat, and gave him such a smash on the head that he fell down. Then one of the Knights drew his sword and killed him dead.

When they saw Wat fall his own men got furious. "Come on," they cried, "come on. They've killed our Captain. Let's kill them all." And they began running towards the King with their bows and arrows.

But Richard wasn't frightened. Instead of running away he rode right in among them. "Men, Men," he shouted, "you surely don't want to shoot your King? You've lost your leader. Come on. I'll be your leader. Follow me."

And putting spurs to his horse he rode as fast as he could right out into the Country with all the Riotous Party after him.

Then when he had made them run a good long way and they were all hot and breathless he stopped and talked to them. He told them that if they went home quietly they wouldn't be punished for all the harm they had done.

So most of them ran off home as fast as ever they could go.

Richard II begins to do the Ruling

When Uncle John and Uncle Thomas heard how Brave the King had been, and how well he had managed the Rioters, they weren't a bit Pleased.

They caught a good many of the Leaders and hanged them. And they made Parliament say that the Villeins weren't free, whatever the King might say.

When Richard heard about that he got into a furious temper and tore up all the letters he'd had written. "All Right," he cried; "they were Slaves and they can remain Slaves for all I care. Oh, I do hate my Uncles! They won't let me do a thing."

At first it looked as if Wat the Tyler hadn't done any good with all his Rioting. But he had. For it was just No Good Parliament saying that the farm workers weren't to go free, because a lot of Farmers found that they could make far more Money out of Wool than out of Corn. So instead of growing corn they began to keep sheep and they didn't need so many men. Then they told their Villeins, "We don't need you. You can go and look for work at some other farm." And in that and other ways, in time, all the workers became Free Men.

"I think we ought to get that boy married," said Uncle John one day. "It might keep him from meddling with the Ruling."

So they got the little Princess Anne of Bohemia to come and be married to King Richard, who was just fifteen.

Anne was the Granddaughter of that King of Bohemia whose Crest and Motto the Black Prince had taken for his own. And Richard liked to remember that her Crest and Motto were the same as his dear Father's had been. She wasn't as beautiful as a Fairy Princess, but she was a perfect Darling, so gentle and good that everyone loved her.

After she came King Richard was a lot happier than he had been. For he loved Anne ever so much and he felt that now at last he'd got a real friend and companion, who couldn't be taken away from him.

At last Richard got tired for of being bullied and managed, and not being allowed to do any Ruling. So one day all of a sudden he said, "Uncles, how old am I?"

"Your Highness is getting on for twenty-two," said one of his Uncles.

"Well then I'm quite old enough to do the Ruling. And I'm going to do it. So, thank you very much, I shan't want you any more."

Then for a bit Richard did the Ruling quite nicely. He made a Truce with France, for of course the Hundred Years War was still going on.

However, the good times didn't last very long. For Richard spent a dreadful lot of money and was always asking for more. He seemed always to be quarrelling with somebody too and soon the people didn't like him much.

Richard II and Little Queen Isabella

Sad to say, Richard's darling Queen Anne died and Richard was most dreadfully sorry. He cried as if he would never stop.

After a bit people began to say that he should marry another Queen. "I won't," said Richard. "I can't bear to think of anyone else taking the place of my dear Anne."

But they kept on and on at him till he couldn't be bothered with them any more. So at last he said, "All right, I'll marry Princess Isabella of France."

"But you can't. She's only a little girl not eight years old. We want you to marry a proper Grown-up Lady."

"Well, I just won't," said Richard, Very Determined. "It's Isabella or No One."

What Richard thought deep down in himself was that in this way he'd get out of marrying anyone. Isabella would be like a daughter to him and it would be nice to have a little girl about the house, for he had no children.

So tall handsome Richard went over to France and was married to little Isabella. Then he brought her back to England. She lived mostly at Windsor Castle. There every day she did her lessons just like any other little girl with her governess. But very often Richard came to see her. Then of course there were no more lessons that day and they had great fun together just like Father and Daughter. For however cruel and Bad-Tempered Richard was with other people he was always gentle and loving to Isabella.

Richard had kind of forgiven his Uncles, but now he was told that Uncle Thomas of Gloucester was plotting against him and that he was going to seize little Isabella and shut her up in Prison.

So he sent for Sir Richard Whittington, who was Lord Mayor of London. "Dick," he said, "I'm going to Pleshy, my Uncle's Castle. I'm going to catch him there and Banish him. I want you to help me with those Retainers of yours – Trained Bands you call them."

"Certainly, your Majesty," said Dick Whittington, "anything to oblige you."

So off Richard went to Pleshy with Dick Whittington's Trained Band, took Uncle Thomas Prisoner, and Banished him to Calais.

There he very soon died in Mysterious Circumstances.

Richard did a lot more Banishings. Among them he banished his Cousin Henry to France for ten years. Henry was his Uncle John Duke of Lancaster's son. But he hadn't been gone three months when his Father, John of Gaunt, died. And Richard stole all his land and money.

Then, as the Irish had been doing some Rebelling (there were always being Bothers in Ireland), he went off there to try to stop them.

Before he started he went to say goodbye to his Little Queen. But she didn't want him to go. She threw her arms round his neck and clung tight to him. "Oh, Richard, dear Richard," she said, "don't go."

"I must, my darling, I must go."

Then Richard took her in his arms and kissed and comforted her until she dried her tears and tried to smile. And he, because he was a big Grown-up Man, tried not to cry. And so at last he went.

But the poor little Queen was not really comforted and for a fortnight she almost made herself sick with crying. She couldn't know it then, but it was the last time that she was to see her tall, kind husband.

When Richard had gone off to Ireland someone went and told Henry, "Richard has gone and stolen all your lands and money."

That made Henry (who was now Duke of Lancaster) dreadfully angry. "If Cousin Richard thinks that I am going to stand that," he said, "he's jolly well mistaken. Come on," he said to the other Banished Lords and Barons who were with him, "come on, I'm going to England to make Richard give everything back to me. Will you come?"

"Rather," they all said.

Then they got into a ship and sailed away for England and landed at Ravenspur in Yorkshire.

There were only fifteen of them, but a Whole Lot of People had been very Fond of Henry. So when they heard that he had come Home they ran as fast as they could to meet him. Soon Henry had an enormous army.

When Richard heard of all these Goings-On he came hurrying back from Ireland as fast as ever he could come. He brought a whole lot of Soldiers with him and meant to fight for his Crown and Throne.

But as soon as they landed nearly all the Soldiers went off and joined Henry and poor Richard found himself left all alone. Even his dog went off to Henry wagging his tail and barking with joy!

All Richard's Servants went too, so he had no one to cook his dinner or make his bed. He felt terribly sad and lonely. "No one loves me," he thought, "I might just as well Give Up. If Henry wants the Throne he can have it."

So when Henry came to see Richard he said quite meekly, "Well, Cousin Lancaster, do what you like. What pleases you will please me."

"You'd better come to London with me then," said Henry. "I hear that you have been ruling Very Badly. We must change that."

So Richard went to London with Henry. And Henry put him in prison and made himself King.

And Richard soon died in prison in Mysterious Circumstances.

All this time the little Queen Isabella didn't know what was happening or why she was never allowed to see Richard. Now she was told, "Your husband is dead and you are a widow."

Isabella was very, very sad when she was told that. She was too sad even to cry. "Please, I want to go home to Mother," she said.

But Henry didn't want her to go. He had always been fond of her. Indeed no one could help being fond of her, she was so lovely and had such pretty ways.

So Henry said, "Don't go away. Stay here and when you're a little older (she was nearly twelve by this time) you could marry my son the Prince of Wales."

"Never, Never, NEVER!" cried Isabella. "I hate you. I hate Prince Hal. If it hadn't been for you, my dear Richard would still be alive. He would still be King of England. Please let me go home to Mother."

"All right," said Henry quite kindly, "you shall go."

So the little Queen of England went back to her Father and Mother the King and Queen of France.

Wyclif and the First English Bible

While Edward III was going on with his rather Silly Wars, and Richard II was chopping off heads and banishing people, something Really Great was happening in England. The Bible was being put into English.

Up to now all the Bibles had been written in Latin and even Top Barons and people like that, who had begun to learn how to read by now, couldn't read the Bible because they didn't know Latin. Only Learned Men and People belonging to the Church could read Latin. They knew how to speak it too because all the Services were said in Latin. But of course Ordinary People couldn't understand what was being said.

"Quite right too," said all the Top Church Persons. "What do Ordinary People want to Understand about Religion for? Their Duty is to do as they are told and not ask Questions. As for reading the Bible – Certainly not. It isn't for them."

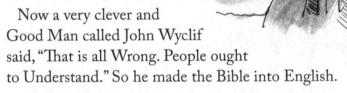

Now a very clever and Good Man called John Wyclif said, "That is all Wrong. People ought to Understand." So he made the Bible into English.

A lot of Top Church Persons were very angry with him (especially the Pope). But Wyclif didn't care. He went about teaching people the Bible. He told them too that the Pope wasn't such a Very Top Person as he seemed to think he was, and that he really hadn't any Right to Make Kings obey him as he wanted them to do.

A lot of People began to think like Wyclif, but most of the Top Persons just laughed at them. They called them 'Lollards' which means Babblers. "For," they said, "these people just go about babbling nonsense." This was really the beginning of there being two Churches, the Roman Catholic and the Protestant Church.

Henry IV of Bolingbroke.
A Whole Lot of Bothers

Richard II was the last of the real Yellow Broom Kings – The Plantagenets.

The next three Kings are generally called Lancastrians because Henry IV was Duke of Lancaster before he made himself King. He was also called Henry of Bolingbroke because he was born there.

He had really No Business to make himself King, because he wasn't the Real Heir. The Real Heir was his kind of Nephew Edmund Mortimer. But Edmund was only seven years old and no one wanted another Boy-King. So Henry quickly sent him to Windsor, where he kept him in a rather comfortable sort of Prison.

Henry's Troubles and Bothers began Almost at Once. Some of the Top Barons who had helped him were sorry they had done it and they wanted to have Richard back again. So they started Rebelling.

"Well," said Henry to himself, "if Richard was dead they couldn't want him back. He'd better be dead." So poor Richard, as you know, died in prison in Mysterious Circumstances.

But still a lot of the Top Barons kept on Rebelling. So the Betrayings and Banishings and Cutting off of Heads began all over again.

Then there was Bother with Wales. Edward I thought that he had Conquered Wales, but of course he hadn't really. And every now and again the Welsh began Rebelling. They did it quite a lot in Henry IV's time.

Now just as if he hadn't enough Bothers already with Rebellings in England and Rebellings in Wales, Henry IV had a try at Conquering in Scotland too. He marched right up to Edinburgh. But that didn't do Any Good. He just had to march back again. Then the Scots had a go at the English and joined up with the English Rebels against Henry. But they didn't do any good either. Henry beat both the Scots and the English Rebels at the Battle of Shrewsbury. And that was the end of that.

Then there was France. The Hundred Years' War was still supposed to be going on, but really there wasn't much fighting there. The French and English just grumbled and growled at each other across the Channel, and were always quarrelling about Something or Other.

So altogether Henry hadn't a Very Happy or Comfortable Reign.

Henry didn't sit on his uncomfortable Throne for very long. He wasn't really old, but he just got tired with all the Bothers and Troubles he had. So he went and died.

Henry V. Madcap Hal becomes Henry V of Monmouth

The Prince of Wales was called Henry like his Father. He was a regular Scamp. He was always getting into Scrapes and doing such Wild Things that he was called Madcap Hal.

Madcap Hal was the next King, and as soon as he turned into Henry V he became a Changed Man. But at first all his old Low Companions came buzzing round. They thought that Henry would just carry on as before. And they hoped that he would make them into Dukes and Barons, and give them easy places at Court so that they'd have nothing to do for the rest of their lives except be Rich and Idle and have a Grand Time.

But Henry shook his head at them. "No," he said, "that's all done with now. I've no time to go Revelling with you any more. I've got to stay at home and see to the Ruling and be a Good King. And you'd better try to behave yourselves in future. If you don't you'll probably end your days in Prison."

So they went off feeling very disgusted. "Who'd have thought it?" they said. "He used to be such a Sport and now he's gone all goody-goody."

Henry V was called Henry of Monmouth because he was born at Monmouth, and as you see he began his Ruling very well. But of course he hadn't any More Right to be King than his Father had. So a whole lot of the Wild Barons began Rebelling and making Bothers, and tried to put the Real Heir on the Throne.

However, Henry soon settled them. Then he began to think about doing some more Conquering in France.

Henry V goes Conquering in France

"It's silly," said Henry to himself, "*calling* myself King of France and not *being* it. What's the good of having two Crowns and only one Throne? There's the Hundred Years' War still going on. I'd better try and make it go on a bit faster. Those Wild Barons too. If they went Conquering in France I wouldn't have as many Bothers with them at home."

So he said to them, "I think we'll go and do some conquering in France."

"Hurrah!" said the Fierce Barons. "Now we can have a Real Good Go at the Frenchies!"

So off they went Rampaging and Conquering in France. They did a lot of little Battles and one big one called Agincourt. It was one of the Biggest Battles ever fought between the French and the English.

The French had far more soldiers than the English. But all the same the English won and they took hundreds and hundreds of the French soldiers Prisoners. But after the Battle the English soldiers were so tired and hungry that they couldn't fight any

more. So Henry took them all home to
England to have a good rest and a
good feed on Good Roast Beef.

While the English soldiers
were having a good Rest and
lots of Good Roast Beef the
French were having a Dreadful
Time all on Their Own. Their
poor King went mad and they
started having a Civil War.
You know what sort of
War that is – half the
Frenchmen were
fighting against
the other half.

Then when Henry
came back to France with
his army just bursting with Health and Spirits, the half of the
Frenchmen who were called Burgundians joined up with him to
fight the other half.

For two or three years the Burgundians and the English went
Rampaging and Conquering all over France until at last the
other half of the Frenchmen got badly beaten.

Then the Burgundians said to Henry, "Now you can be King
of France."

But Henry had seen Princess Catherine the French King's
daughter. He thought that she was the Most Beautiful Lady in
the Whole Wide World and he wanted to marry her. "That will
be the best way of joining England and France," he said. "I'll
marry Princess Catherine. I'll let her Father be King till he dies
and then I'll be King. But I'll begin doing the Ruling now, for of
course a mad King can't really do any Ruling."

So it was arranged like that. And no one seemed to think that the French King's son who was called the Dauphin might have something to say about it.

Then there was ever such a grand wedding in Paris and Catherine of France became Queen of England.

Even after he was married Henry went on with his Conquering for he wanted to beat the rest of the French who would have liked the Dauphin to be their King. Then one day when he was out in the wet and the cold East Wind he caught a dreadful cold. It got so bad that he had to send for the Doctor.

When he came the Doctor looked very grave. "Why, Your Majesty, you've got Pleurisy," he said.

And the pleurisy got so bad that poor Henry died. So after all he was never King of France.

Everyone had loved King Henry. He was so young and handsome and had such a lovely smile and nice ways. He did the Ruling well too. So we only have to give him One Bad Mark. It's rather a Big Black Mark. He had no Business to go Conquering in France. It was silly, and wicked as well. The only excuse for him is that people hadn't learnt in those days that going stealing Other People's Crowns and Thrones and Things wasn't at all a nice way to behave. They hadn't learnt that it is just as bad as breaking into somebody's house and stealing their silver spoons or best silver teapot or something.

Of course people know better now.

Henry VI. The Maid of Orleans

Henry VI was only a little Baby when he became King of England, so of course he didn't know anything about it. Then in a Very few weeks the King of France died, so baby Henry was called, "King by the Grace of God of France and of England." Poor little Baby, with two great heavy Golden Crowns to wear!

However, Henry had an Uncle, John, Duke of Bedford. He wasn't such a bad uncle and he sent the Baby King home to England and did the Ruling in France. But of course he hadn't any more Business to rule in France than Henry V had had. And he soon began to have lots of Bothers.

The Dauphin was a poor Mutt. He hadn't even oomph enough to go and get himself Crowned and be called Charles VII by the Grace of God King of France. He just played about and amused himself and Let Things Slide.

But there were still a Faithful Few who loved France and who were ready to die for their Country. "The Dauphin may be a Poor Thing," they said, "but he is Our Own. He's a Frenchman and that's better than an English Baby anyhow."

So they gathered all their Fierce Retainers and fought Uncle John and his English like anything. But it didn't seem to be Much Use. They got beaten again and again.

Then when things seemed to be just as bad as they could be, help came. Far far away from the Raging Rampaging armies, in a quiet little French village, there lived a girl called Joan of Arc. Her Father and Mother were very poor so Joan was not taught to read or write. She just helped her Mother about the house and went out into the fields to look after her Father's sheep. She was Good and Obedient. She loved her Father and Mother and Brothers and Sisters very much. But more than them all she loved France.

There were no newspapers in those days, but sometimes wounded Soldiers would come to the little Village. Sitting round the fire in the evenings they would tell stories about the dreadful quarrels that were going on between the French and the English.

All these stories hurt Joan dreadfully. She felt that she just couldn't bear to have an English Baby for her King. She couldn't bear to think of the Good Frenchmen getting killed. And the more she thought the more she felt that Something Must be Done About It.

Then it seemed to her that Saints and Angels came and spoke to her. "Joan," they said, "it is you who must Do Something About It. You must save France."

But Joan was frightened. "What can I do?" she asked. "I'm only seventeen. I don't know anything about Fighting and Conquering."

"That doesn't matter," said the Voices. "You have been chosen to do this Great Thing. Now go and do it."

So Joan told her Father and Mother, "I'm going to the War to save France from the English."

"Oh, Joan," they said. "Don't talk such Nonsense. How can a girl like you save France?"

"I don't know yet," said Joan, "but the Saints and Angels have told me to go and I'm going."

So she got on a horse and rode hundreds and hundreds of Miles across France until she came to where the Battle was.

"Please," she said, when she got there, "take me to the Dauphin."

So a man showed her the way to the Castle where the Dauphin was amusing himself, singing and dancing with a lot of Cowardly Knights and Nobles, and not caring a bit how much his Poor People were being hurt.

Joan knelt down beside the Dauphin and took his hand. "Gentle Dauphin," she said, "why do you stay here singing and dancing when your poor Country is in such trouble? Why don't you go and fight? Why don't you go and get crowned? I have been sent to help you to Fight and to Conquer."

"How old are you?" asked someone.

"Seventeen."

"What do you know about Fighting and Conquering?"

"Nothing," said Joan.

"Have you ever seen a Battle?" asked someone else.

Then they all roared with laughter at her. "Here's an ignorant country girl who's never even seen a Battle come to teach us how to Fight and Conquer," they cried. "It's too comic for words."

"See here," said the Dauphin, "get rid of the girl. Give her what she wants, only get rid of her."

So they gave her some soldiers and a lovely white horse to ride on, a white silk banner with beautiful things painted on it, and shining armour.

"Now," said Joan, "I want My Sword."

So they brought her a sword.

"No," said Joan. "Not that sword. I want my Own. I'll tell you where it is."

Then she told them it was hidden behind the altar in a Church some distance away. So a messenger was sent to look for it. And he found it exactly where Joan said it was. It was very old and all red-rusty.

So they cleaned it with sand and oil till it shone like new.

"Now," said Joan when she had buckled it on, "I'm ready. Let's go to the War."

And off she went at the head of her men, riding on her white horse and carrying her white flag in her hand.

They rode to Orleans which the English were trying to take away from the Faithful Few. When they got there Joan spoke to her soldiers.

"I have come," she said, "to lead you to Victory."

"By gum!" said a soldier in astonishment.

"Now," said Joan. "We must chase these English away."

And chase them away they did. In about a week Orleans was free from them, and from that day Joan was called The Maid of Orleans.

After Orleans had been freed from the English Joan went on her gallant way leading her Army from Victory to Victory, and beating the English over and over again. She was teaching the French to Love their Country. And she taught them so well that they have never forgotten the lesson.

Very soon the French had won back a whole lot of the towns that the English had taken. They had won back such a lot that it was quite safe for the Dauphin to go to the Great Cathedral at Reims to be crowned. But he was so lazy that he just couldn't be bothered. He made all sorts of excuses not to. But Joan made him go.

"Dear Dauphin," she said, "don't you see? Until you are crowned the People won't believe that you are really and truly King of France. They will still think that that English Baby is their King. Now be good and come and be crowned."

"Oh, well," said the Dauphin crossly, "anything for Peace and Quiet." And he went.

Joan stood beside him while he was being Crowned. She wore her shining armour and held her white banner in her hand.

Then when all the rejoicing was over, when the people had cheered themselves hoarse and danced holes in their Slippers, Joan began to say Goodbye to her friends.

"But why are you saying Goodbye?" they asked.

"Because my Work is done," she told them. "Orleans is saved, France is awake and the King is sitting on his Throne. So I'm going home to help my Mother about the house. I've not been home for about six months now and I know she must be missing me. Father too, he'll want me to help with the sheep. So I must go."

But the Soldiers loved their Maid just terribly.

"Oh, dear Maid," they begged, "stay with us, stay with us. Oh, don't go away. Oh, do say that you will stay with us."

So at last Joan Gave In and said she'd stay. Then ever so pleased, the French went on again chasing the English away and winning back lots More of France.

Then one sad day Joan was wounded and taken Prisoner. Oh! that indeed was a Sad Day for the French. But the English were glad, just ever so glad.

"Now that they've lost their Witch," they said, "we'll easily beat the Frenchies."

But it just didn't happen like that. The French fought as hard as ever. "Joan would want us to," they said, "and even if she isn't here we must do as she says."

Then, finding that they weren't getting on any better, the English said, "If the Witch was dead she couldn't help them any more. We'd better Kill her." So they Killed her.

Oh, what a shame it was of the English to go and kill the Glorious Maid! But they made a Great Mistake in thinking they'd get on better if Joan were out of the way. For the French were just Furious with them. They fought harder than ever. And at last they chased the English right out of France. Of all their Conquerings not one bit of France remained to them, not one Town except Calais. The French just let them keep that. And so the Hundred Years' War came to an end.

People have mostly forgotten about the Hundred Years' War. It doesn't seem to matter much now. But they have never forgotten about the Maid of Orleans. And hundreds of years later, after another dreadful wicked War, the Pope made her into a Saint. So now she is Saint Joan of Arc. And in every Church in France you can see her Statue with flowers in front of it and people kneeling there to say their Prayers.

Henry VI. The Baby King Grows Up

It took the French Years and Years to chase all the English out of France. For as you know Englishmen are not Easy to Beat even when they are in the Wrong.

While the French were busy chasing the English away, the Baby King Henry VI was Growing Up.

He was a quiet little boy with good manners and a nice smile, who was rather stupid at doing his lessons although he liked doing them.

But when Henry got to being Grown Up it was seen that he wouldn't be Much Good as a King. He didn't seem to have any Will of his Own and he just couldn't manage the Fierce Barons a bit. They managed him and did as they liked with him, making him say one thing one day and something quite different the next.

The Fierce Barons grew Fiercer and Fiercer and things got into a jolly fine Mess. So Betrayings and Banishings and Cutting Off Heads became quite Common.

Among other things the Barons made Henry marry a French Lady called Margaret of Anjou. The English Kings were always quarrelling with the French, but all the same they had quite a habit of marrying French Ladies.

Margaret was a very Managing Lady. She managed the King, she managed the Kingdom, and she wanted to manage all the Fierce Barons. "We don't mind obeying the King more or less," they said. "But obeying a woman, and a French one at that! That's quite another matter."

So they began Rebelling, and then Richard Duke of York said, "Really you know this can't be allowed to go on. If Cousin Henry can't make a better show of Ruling than this, I Must Take a Hand. I've really far more Right to be King than he has, and I could do it much better."

Richard Duke of York said that because he was the Great-great-ever-so-many-Greats-Grandson of Edward III. A whole lot of people thought as he did. So soon everyone was Taking Sides, some sticking up for the King and others for the Duke of York.

Henry VI. Red Roses and White Roses

One day the Duke of York was having a dinner-party at the Temple in London. Before dinner he and his guests strolled about in the garden with a lot more Barons and Nobles. Richard went about talking to them all and trying to make them say which Side they were on. "Don't you think really and truly I've a better Right to be King than Henry has?" he asked. But everyone was rather afraid of answering a Dangerous Question like that.

"Tut, tut," said Richard, getting impatient, "I see what it is, you're all afraid to speak. Cowardy Custards that's what you are. Well you needn't say anything. Look here. Do you see this White Rose?" And he gathered a rose off the bush beside him. "A White Rose is going to be my Badge – my Sign. And anyone who is on my side has only got to put a White Rose in his hat."

"And anyone who is true to the King has only got to put a Red Rose in his hat-band," said another Baron, tearing a Red Rose from another bush.

After that all the Barons who were there began putting Red Roses or White Roses in their hats, quarrelling like anything and being rude to each other.

At last they all went away, yelling rude things at each other as they went down the street.

"Well, well," said Richard, "I know now who is on my side and who isn't. Come on, let's go and have some dinner."

And a nice sight the Temple Garden must have been after they'd gone, with all the flower-beds trampled and the rose bushes broken to bits. Just imagine what it would be like if a whole lot of rowdy young lords and nobles began stealing the roses in Regent's Park. The Police would soon be after them, and some of them would very likely get themselves landed in Prison.

But in those days there were no Proper Police and the Fierce Barons just carried on how they liked.

The quarrel didn't end with a brawl in Temple Gardens. Very soon it became a Civil War and you know what Kind of War that is. It was called the War of the Roses, because the soldiers on the side of Lancaster, that is the King's side, wore red roses in their helmets. The Duke of York's soldiers wore white ones. Of course they weren't Real Roses. They were made of wool, some White and some dyed Red.

Both armies went Rampaging up and down the Country, fighting battles here, there, and everywhere. Sometimes the Red Roses would win, sometimes the White Roses would win.

Although Richard Duke of York had started all the Rebelling he wasn't really such a Bad Man as you might think. He might have made a better King than Henry. But in one of the Battles he got Killed. That, however, didn't end the war. For Richard had a son called Edward and he carried on. Edward wasn't a very nice man. But he was young and handsome and a whole lot of people liked him.

So one day when he arrived at London with his army the people were delighted to see him. They came crowding round him cheering like mad.

Then when he could make himself heard for the row, a bishop got up and made a speech. "You've all been very miserable having Henry for your King," he said. "Do you still want him to go on being King?"

"No! no! no!" shouted everyone.

"Would you like Edward to be King?"

"Yes! yes! yes!" they yelled. "Let's have Edward. King Edward! King Edward! Long live King Edward!"

And that's how Edward Duke of York became Edward IV King of England.

CHAPTER IX · WHITE ROSE KINGS

Edward IV and the King-Maker

The People at London had chosen Edward for their King, but he wasn't sitting at all comfortably on the Throne. For Henry was still King too. Of course the English didn't want there to be two Kings. So they went on fighting about it.

And really the way they carried on sounds more like a Make-Believe Story than a True one. In the next Battle the Red Roses got beaten, and Henry and the Managing Margaret ran away to Scotland. Henry would have liked just to stay there quietly. "Don't you think, my dear," he said to Margaret, "I'd better give up the Throne seeing Edward wants it so very much?"

"Don't be a Fool, Henry," she cried. "Give Up the Throne! Certainly Not."

And she rushed off to France and came back with another army which she'd got the French King to give her.

She got dreadfully beaten again, and once more ran away to France. But she left poor Henry behind, and Edward got hold of him and put him in Prison. With Henry in Prison Edward felt that he was pretty safely seated on the Throne and that he could now think of settling down and having some Peace and Quiet.

So he married a beautiful Lady called Elizabeth Woodville.

When the Top Barons heard about it they were very angry, for they didn't think she was Good Enough to be their Queen. She wasn't a Royal Princess. She wasn't even a Duchess. She was just an Ordinary Lady. So they turned up their Noses at her.

Richard Earl of Warwick was more angry than all the others put together. He had done more than anyone else to help Edward to get safely seated on the Throne and he had just been planning a Good Marriage for Edward, with one of the French Princesses.

He got so furious at last that he took Edward and put him in Prison. So there were two Kings of England and they were both in Prison! Then Warwick did the Ruling all by himself for a year.

After that Warwick forgave Edward. He let him out of Prison and they shook hands and made it up. But they couldn't keep being friends for long, and the next time they quarrelled Warwick went off to Managing Margaret, who was living in France, and told her, "I'm tired of the way Edward is going on. So if you'd like to get another army and come to help me fight I'll let Henry out of Prison and make him King again."

"Thank you," said Margaret, "I'll certainly come. You go along and let Henry out of Prison. And I'll join you as soon as I can get an army together."

So back Warwick went to England and took Henry out of Prison and dressed him up in Grand Clothes. Then the poor King was put on a horse and led through the Streets of London while the People cheered and shouted, "King Henry! King Henry! Long live King Henry!"

And because Warwick kept on making Kings, and un-making them again, just as he liked, he got called "The King-Maker."

While the people were looking out their old Red Roses and sticking them in their caps and cheering King Henry, Edward said to himself, "Well, after all, the Throne of England isn't as safe a seat as I thought it was. I'd better be going." So he ran away to Holland.

He arrived there without a penny to bless himself with, with nothing indeed but the clothes he wore.

But Edward made friends with the Duke of Burgundy who

was married to his sister Margaret. So he soon got plenty of new clothes and soldiers too.

You remember the Burgundians had been on the English side at the time of the Maid of Orleans. So now the Duke gathered a lot of Soldiers together and gave them to Edward. Then back to England went Edward and landed at Ravenspur. Then another great Battle was fought between the Red Roses and the White Roses. The White Roses won and the King-Maker got killed.

The very next day Managing Margaret landed with her army. It was too late. But she wasn't going to Give Up. Not she. So there was another Grand Battle. Again the White Roses won. That was the end of it. Into Prison went Queen Margaret and back to Prison went poor Henry. There a few days later he died in Mysterious Circumstances. Margaret stayed in Prison for two or three years. Then the King of France paid Edward a lot of money to let her come out and go to France. There she lived quietly and didn't try to Manage Kings and Peoples any more.

Now that Edward's enemies were all dead or in Prison he had a chance of settling down and doing some Ruling. He didn't think about the good-of-his-People. He thought more of having a Good Time for himself. But he was very fond of his wife Queen Elizabeth and of his children, and of all the Queen's relatives too. That, however, didn't please the Top Barons. For the Queen's relatives weren't Top Barons but just quite Ordinary.

The Queen's brother, however, who was called Lord Rivers, was a very learned man. Edward liked him, and as he wanted his little son Edward, Prince of Wales to grow up into a good wise man he asked Uncle Rivers to teach him.

One day when Uncle Rivers was talking to the King he asked him, "Have you seen the new machine that's been invented for printing?"

"What do you mean? What's printing?" asked the King.

"Instead of writing books by hand there's a new machine for doing it. It will do pages and pages all at once. And you can make ever so many copies in no time. It is really very wonderful and books will be a lot cheaper. You really ought to go and see it."

It's hard to read but I think this is CAXTON'S Press

Dodgy Logo..

"Where can I see it?" asked the King. "It does sound wonderful. Who does it?"

"A Master William Caxton. He's been living in Flanders. He's come home now and set up his machine at the Sign of the Red Pale here in Westminster. It's quite near. If you're not busy just put on your hat and we could go and see him now."

"I'd like to," said the King. And he and Uncle Rivers set off to see Master William Caxton and his wonderful machine.

Edward thought it marvellous and after that he often used to go to talk to Master William Caxton and watch the work.

And of all the Things in Edward IV's reign, the beginning of printing is the Best Thing to remember. But peaceful things like printing didn't interest Edward for long. He was just a jolly handsome brute, much more interested in Fighting and Conquering than in anything to do with learning. And he was just setting off to do some more Conquering in France when he died.

Edward V. The King who Never Did Any Ruling

Ever since Edward, Prince of Wales had been quite a tiny boy Uncle Rivers had taken care of him and taught him. He had a lot of lessons to do, reading and writing and grammar and music and Ordinary Things like that. Besides these kinds of things Uncle Rivers taught him all about the Duties-of-a-Prince-towards-his-People, and all sorts of things that a King, if he is to be a Good King, must know. So that he was kept very busy, but between Supper and Bedtime, at eight o'clock, was Playtime. Then he played games and had great fun with Uncle Rivers and with the other little boys who were taught with him.

Some time before King Edward IV died there had been a lot of Bother with Wales. So King Edward said to Uncle Rivers, "I think that you and Edward had better go to live in Ludlow Castle. It's quite close to Wales and perhaps the Welsh will behave a little better if they have their own Prince living near them." So the Prince of Wales and Uncle Rivers went off to Ludlow.

They were still living at Ludlow when a messenger arrived. "King Edward IV is dead," he told them. "Long live King Edward V! And the Queen says that he must come to London to be crowned."

Uncle Rivers and King Edward V set off to go to London, but on the way Edward's other uncle, Richard Duke of Gloucester, met them. Richard was a Wicked Uncle. He put Uncle Rivers and all the little King's friends in Prison and took charge of him himself. Poor Edward cried like anything for he loved Uncle Rivers and he was afraid of Uncle Richard with his ugly face.

"Oh, please, Uncle, I want to stay with Uncle Rivers," he begged.

"Well, you just can't. You've got to go to London to be Crowned."

So to London Edward went with his Wicked Uncle Richard.

Now that he had got hold of the King, Richard wanted to get hold of his other Nephew, Richard, Duke of York.

But when Queen Elizabeth heard what Uncle Richard had done she got frightened and ran away to Westminster to hide from him. She took all her other children with her too in case he should get hold of any of them. The place she went to hide in was called The Sanctuary.

A Sanctuary means a Holy Place and if you got there no one could touch you. It was rather like a game of It. If you got to the Sanctuary you were "home".

Of course Uncle Richard was Very Much Annoyed when he heard that the Queen had gone there. So he sent the Archbishop of Canterbury to tell her not to be so silly. "Tell her," he said, "that it is very unkind of her to keep Richard away from his brother. They haven't seen each other for ever so long and Edward is lonely without him."

Queen Elizabeth listened to what the Archbishop had to say, then she told him, "Yes, of course the boys should be together. You'd better send Edward here."

"Oh, I can't do that," said the Archbishop. "King Edward has to be Crowned, and of course Prince Richard must go to the Coronation."

"Well, he just can't go," said the Queen. "Dickie has been ill. He's not well enough to go."

So they talked and talked and the Queen wouldn't give way. At last the Archbishop told her, "Look here. I'll look after the boy; he'll be quite safe with me."

So Queen Elizabeth let him go.

When Wicked Uncle Richard saw the little Prince he grinned all over his horrid ugly face. "So here you are at last, my boy," he said. "I'm very glad to see you, and Edward will be very glad too."

Then he took both the boys to the Tower of London, and shut them up in a room together. As soon as he'd got the King and his Brother safely locked up Uncle Richard began to Plot. "I really ought to be King," he told everybody. "A Boy-King's no Good. He'll only make a Mess of Things. You'd much better make me King."

He talked such a lot and Plotted such a lot that people began to think, "Really it's rather a Good Idea. Let's have Richard."

So they all shouted, "King Richard! King Richard! Long live King Richard!" Then Richard went and got himself Crowned King and his wife Anne crowned Queen, while the True King was playing games with his little brother in the Tower of London.

Edward never ruled. He was never crowned. Still we count him among our Kings and call him Edward V. He reigned only about three months and most of that time he spent as a prisoner in the Tower of London.

Richard III. A Bold Bad Villain

Richard III now wore the Crown and was seated on the Throne. But he wasn't a bit comfortable. "There are those two boys in the Tower," he said to himself. "One of these days people will start Rebelling and wanting to make Edward King. I'd better just kill him and Richard too. I'd feel safer then."

He sent for a Bad Man (he knew plenty of Bad Men).

"Just go to the Governor of the Tower," he told him, "and tell him that I've made you Governor for a day. Get all the Keys from him. And when you've got them you might just kill the two Princes that are there. I'll give you a lot of money if you do it well."

The Bad Man was quite pleased as he was used to doing Wicked Things like Killing people. And when he'd got the keys of the Tower he went to the room where the Princes were sleeping. They both slept in the same bed with their arms round each other's necks. So it was quite easy for the Bad Man. He just took the pillows and smothered them.

Then he went and told the King, "I've done it. Can I have my money now, please?"

"Ah!" said Richard, "that's good: I feel more comfortable now."

But he wasn't comfortable for long. For when the People heard what he'd done they began to hate him like Poison. Even the Top Barons who had helped most to get him seated on the Throne began to hate him. Then Richard saw that he'd made a Bad Mistake. So he began to try to Curry Favour with everybody by making some Good Laws. But it wasn't any use; they just went on hating him.

Then some of the Top Barons got together and Plotted. "We really can't go on having a Bold Bad Villain like this for our King," said one. "Let's try someone else."

"Well, there's Henry Tudor, Earl of Richmond. What about him?"

"That's a Good Idea. He has about as good a Right to be King as anyone else. Let's try him."

You remember that Henry V married a beautiful French Princess called Catherine, and then he went and got Pleurisy and died. After that Queen Catherine came to live in England, and when she got tired of being a widow she married a Welsh Gentleman called Owen Tudor. This Henry Tudor, Earl of Richmond was her Grandson. He was also an ever-so-many-greats-Grandson of John of Gaunt. So it did seem as if he had some Right to the Throne.

Having settled it between themselves the Top Barons went to Henry. "Would you like to come and be our King?" they asked him.

"Yes, thank you, I should very much," said Henry.

"Come on then," they said. "Get some soldiers together. We'll get as many as we can as well and we'll fight Richard for the Crown."

Richard gathered his soldiers too and they had a Battle called the Battle of Bosworth Field. Richard was Bad and Cruel, but he was brave in a kind of way. So he fought like a Tiger Cat. All the same he got killed. The Crown fell off his head and rolled away under a May tree. One of the Top Barons saw it there and picked it up.

"Hullo," he said, "I've found the Crown. Where's Henry?"

So they got hold of Henry Tudor and put the Crown on his head. Then all the Barons and Knights and Soldiers crowded round him shouting, "King Henry! King Henry! Long live King Henry!"

That was the end of the Wars of the Roses, and Richard was the last of the White Rose Kings. He had sat on the Throne for Two years and Two months and a day. "Twenty-six months and twenty-four hours too long," said one of the first people to write about him.

Henry VII. A Very Careful King

We've had British Kings, English Kings, Norman Kings, Kings who were half-English, half-Norman, Kings who were half-English with a lot of French and a bit of Scotch; all sorts of Kings. Now we have a new kind of King, for Henry VII was half-Welsh, a bit English, and a little bit French. He was called Henry Tudor and the next two Kings and two Queens were called Tudors too.

Henry VII was the Red Rose Champion and he married Princess Elizabeth who was the White Rose Princess. She was the sister of poor little Edward V. "There now," said most Sensible People, "we needn't quarrel any more for the Red Rose and the White Rose are joined together." But it didn't happen quite like that all at once. For there were still a lot of White Rose Fans about who just couldn't bear to Give In, and they tried to make Mischief.

Except for these Bothers there was mostly Peace and Quiet while Henry VII sat on the Throne.

One reason for the Peace and Quiet was that most of the Top Barons had got killed in the Wars of the Roses. They were the most unruly ones, and the others were quite glad to settle down and be Comfortable. They weren't so Rich as the Top Barons had been, so they couldn't keep so many Fierce Retainers to go Rampaging about the Country with. Besides which Henry wouldn't let them. Like Henry II he said, "If there is to be any War, I'm going to make it, not you." And he fined them if he found that they were keeping more Retainers than he said they might.

That was Henry VII's way of doing things. He wasn't fond of chopping off people's heads, but he was very fond of money. So when any Baron got too unruly he just caught him and told him, "Now look here, you've been most annoying and you deserve to be hanged or to have your head cut off. But I'll let you off this time with a fine."

Henry kept all the fines he made the unruly Barons pay. So he got quite Rich. He took all the Lands and Money of the Barons who had been killed in the Wars of the Roses too. And that made him richer still.

Henry didn't like chopping off people's heads and he didn't like going Conquering and Fighting battles either. In that way the People hadn't to pay such a lot of taxes and they began to get rich too.

In another way Henry was different from most of the Kings who had been before him. They all liked spending Money and often spent far too much. Henry didn't like spending it. He liked keeping it. Perhaps he was Saving Up and Meaning to do something Very Splendid with it all Some Day. If he was, he never told anyone about it, so we shall never know. He just kept on getting more and more money and spending as little as ever he could until at last he was the richest King in all Europe.

Another reason for the Peace and Quiet of Henry's reign was that people had begun to read. Even after printing had been found out books were very dear. Still they were not too dear for some people to buy them. And as more and more got printed they got cheaper and cheaper. So a lot of people found that it was much more Comfortable to sit by the fire and read an exciting book than to go Tramping out in all weathers Fighting and Rampaging about and perhaps getting killed.

Henry VII. How a Sailor Found a New Island

Still another reason for the Peace and Quiet was that people began to learn that if they wanted to risk their lives and have Exciting Adventures they could do it on the Sea instead of on the Land.

In the old Far-off Days people used to think that the world was flat and not round. They thought that if you got to the edge of it you'd fall off into Nowhere. So they were afraid to go too far in case they should fall off. They knew about Europe and Asia, and a little bit about Africa, and that was all.

Then some Wise Men found out that the World wasn't flat but Round. And at last a daring Sailor called Christopher Columbus said to himself, "Well, if the World is Round I could get to India by sailing West instead of East." But that meant going on the Sea of Darkness, which everyone was afraid to do. Most people too thought that the Whole Idea was altogether

THE DEEP

Mad. But at last Christopher got the King and Queen of Spain to listen to him and believe in his Great Idea. He found some sailors, too, daring enough to sail out into the Sea of Darkness with him, and he set off.

For days and weeks he sailed and sailed and at last came to land. He thought he had reached India. But of course he hadn't. He had reached the Islands off the coast of America which we still call the West Indies, although they are nowhere near India. Other daring sailors followed Columbus and after a lot of Voyages it was found out that you couldn't sail to India that way because a great big enormous Continent barred the way. So they called it the New World.

In those days the Spaniards and the Portuguese were the most daring Sailors. They went about making ever such dangerous Voyages, and finding all sorts of islands, and soon they began quarrelling about whom they belonged to.

So they went to the Pope about it. He still thought himself the Most Top Person in all the Wide World, and still had the habit of giving away Thrones and Kingdoms and Things like that.

So now he told them, "You can stop quarrelling. This is what I'll do. I'll make a pretending line down the World from the North to the South. Every new Island or bit of Land found on one side of the line belongs to Spain and every bit on the other side belongs to Portugal."

But when the King of France heard what the Pope had said he was very much annoyed. "Oh, indeed," he said. "I never heard that Adam made a Will leaving all the Unknown Lands to the King of Spain and the King of Portugal. And until I see that Will I shan't take any notice of what the Pope says."

So he too began sending his Sailors out to Cross the Seas in search of new lands. The King of England alone of all the Top Kings (for Henry was getting to be a Very Top King by this time) didn't do anything about it.

Then an Italian called John Cabot, who had been living in England for some time, went to King Henry. "My Lord King," he told him, "if you don't do something these Spaniards and Portuguese will be getting all the Spare Places in the World and there won't be any left for you to get."

"Well," Henry told him, "you can go and look for some if you like."

"Oh, but I'm only a poor sailor," said Cabot. "I haven't got enough money to buy ships with and pay the sailors. I thought perhaps that you would buy me a ship or two and pay for the sailors to go with me. Then if we found any new Islands they'd be yours."

"Oh," Henry told him, "I don't think I can afford to do that. Perhaps you mightn't find any New Land after all. Then my good money would all be wasted. I don't like wasting money."

"Oh, I'm pretty sure I'd find something," said Cabot.

So they talked and talked, and at last Henry told Cabot, "I'll buy you one ship. You must just make that do."

The ship Henry bought was called the *Matthew*, and it was THE FIRST ENGLISH BOAT EVER TO CROSS THE ATLANTIC OCEAN.

I daresay you have seen pictures of the *Queen Mary*. But the *Matthew* wasn't a big ship like that. It was just a little bit of a thing. The *Queen Mary* is more than eight hundred times bigger than the *Matthew*. So you can guess what a tiny ship it was, and what an awfully Big Adventure it was for these eighteen Bristol men to go sailing away on the "Sea of Darkness".

For days and days Cabot sailed along. For a whole month he sailed and still there was nothing to be seen but the sea all round. The sailors were getting very downhearted and had begun grumbling like anything. Then at last one morning they saw the land. Oh, what joy! They all went ashore and skipped and ran about. Then Cabot set up a Big Cross, and a tall pole, with the flag of England on it, and claimed the land for Henry VII, King of England and of France, and Lord of Ireland.

Cabot called his new Island New-Found-Land, and we still call it that.

After all these grand doings Cabot and his sailors turned home again and hardly more than three months after they had set out they were back in Bristol.

The people of Bristol were just terribly excited when they saw the little ship come sailing into the Harbour. They crowded round Cabot listening to the wonderful stories he had to tell.

Even King Henry got excited. And he was so pleased at having a new Island that he gave Cabot Ten Pounds for himself.

And that was the beginning of the British Empire. Henry was really a Great King, although some people think he was mean about money. He may have been. But he did think about the Good-of-his-People.

He saw that if the English were to be a Great and Peace-loving People they must have something to do besides going Fighting and Conquering. So he encouraged them to go Trading with other Countries, as well as scouring the Seas looking for new Islands. Edward III too had encouraged his people to go trading, you remember. So the English began to be a Nation of Shopkeepers, as another King kind of Person called us hundreds of years later.

But the best thing Henry gave his People was some Peace and Quiet. Many of them, however, weren't as grateful about that as they should have been. So they weren't very sorry when he got consumption and died.

Henry VIII. A Jolly King and his Great Chancellor

When people are young they don't always like to be told, "You must do this and you mustn't do that."

So they ask, "Why?"

Unfortunately the answer often is, "Because I say so." That is called "Being Autocratic," which means "I am She (or He) who must be obeyed. So do as you are told, and don't ask Questions."

Being Autocratic is not really a very good way of doing the Ruling. It would be much better if people would explain why. But they just don't.

It was very like that in England at this time. All the Tudors were Autocratic and Henry VII was just as bad at being it as the rest of them.

But the People didn't like just being ordered about. They wanted to know the reason why.

The Barons especially didn't like being kept in order and fined when they disobeyed. Henry II had made them behave, but the Kings who came after him hadn't managed them well. So they had grown more and more Unruly. They had gone about like little Kings, Making War and Making Peace when and where they chose. So when Henry VII told them, "You'll make no more War if you please. You'll Keep the KING'S PEACE," they weren't at all pleased.

So when they got a new King, who was young and jolly, they were all very glad. And they hoped that he would let them do what they liked. But it just didn't happen like that. For Henry VIII was more autocratic even than Henry VII.

Henry VIII was just eighteen when he began being King. He was good-looking and slender, splendid at games and all sorts of sports. He was very fond of going to balls and parties too, and was always flirting with the girls. As for Ruling Justly and looking after the Good-of-his-People! Oh, well, his Top Person (who was, as you know, always called The Chancellor) could look after all that.

Henry VIII's Chancellor was called Wolsey. He was the son of an Ipswich Butcher. But he was very Clever. So he Got On, and became Great. He had made friends with Henry when Henry was Prince of Wales. And Henry loved him so much that when

he became King he made him Chancellor, and Archbishop of Canterbury too, just as Henry II had made Thomas à Becket.

Wolsey soon became a Very Rich Man. He lived in a splendid Palace, wore the grandest clothes of scarlet silk and satin, walked about in golden shoes, and had hundreds of servants.

Wolsey was very Proud and Haughty too, and thought himself grander than any Noble in all the land. And the Nobles and Gentlemen just hated him. They couldn't forget that he was Low-Born and called him that "Jumped-up Butcher Boy," and Things like that.

Henry was as fond of Grand Clothes and gorgeous Palaces as his Chancellor, and as his Father had left him heaps of money he just spent it as fast as he could on having a Jolly Time. Then after a bit he thought he'd better get married.

Henry had had a brother called Arthur, who had married a Spanish Princess called Katherine of Aragon. Very soon after he'd married, Arthur died. But instead of going home to Spain, Princess Katherine stayed on in England. Now Henry thought that it would be rather a Good Idea to marry her. But it was against the Law for him to marry his brother's Widow.

So Henry sent to the Pope and asked him, "Can I marry Princess Katherine?"

And the Pope said, "Yes, you may."

So there was ever such a grand wedding and after it a still grander Coronation, with all sorts of balls and parties.

For a few years things went on quietly. Then Henry got tired of just amusing himself, and thought he'd like to do some fighting and get some Glory. So he set out to do some Conquering in France.

The French and the Scots had always been Friends and James IV and Henry VIII had already been quarrelling. So now James

thought he'd help his French Friends and he marched into
England with a splendid army of Knights and Nobles. But in
a dreadful Battle called Flodden the Scots were beaten, and
King James and nearly all the Scottish Nobles were killed. After
that Henry made Peace with Scotland, for Queen Margaret of
Scotland was his sister and he wasn't really so unkind as to want
to go on fighting his own Sister.

Henry VIII. The Field of the Cloth of Gold

Soon after this, although he hadn't gained much Glory, Henry
made peace with France too. Then Wolsey, who was always
thinking about making England Great (and himself as well), told
Henry, "My Lord King, I think you ought to make friends with
the King of France."

"Oh, you do, do you?" said Henry, making a face. "I'm really
not very keen. But if you think it would be a Wise Thing to do,
I suppose it would be a Wise Thing." For Henry knew what a
clever man Wolsey was and at this time was generally ready to do
anything he said.

"Yes, I think it would be Wise to show the King of France what
a Rich and Splendid Country England is," said Wolsey.

"And how are you going to set about making us Friends?"
asked Henry. For he was very lazy and left everything to his
Chancellor.

"You should have a meeting and have games and sports
together, for Francis is almost as good a Sportsman as Your
Majesty. He is almost as handsome too," Wolsey told the King in
his sly flattering way. "You'd be very well matched. And you could
sometimes let him win."

"Well it seems rather a Good Idea," said Henry. "You'd better arrange it."

So the great Chancellor arranged a meeting between the Two Kings. He arranged that it should be in France, but not in Paris, or any other big town where Francis might have a Palace and make a grander show than the King of England. That wasn't Wolsey's idea at all. He arranged to have it at a little village not far from Calais which still belonged to the English. There he had a splendid new Palace built for Henry. It was only made of wood, but it was gaily painted and gilded all over, so that with its towers and turrets all shining in the sun it looked like a Fairy Palace. It had a gilded fence round it and Golden Gates, and in the middle of a great court there was a golden fountain set with rubies and diamonds and all sorts of precious stones. And, instead of water, white wine and red wine came pouring out of it.

When everything was ready King Francis came from Paris, and King Henry and Queen Katherine sailed over the sea from England. Riding on splendid horses, the two Kings met. They were dressed in gold and silver cloth and glittering with diamonds. When they came quite close they threw their arms round each other's necks and kissed each other. "Dear Brother and Cousin," said Francis, "I have come a long way to see you. I hope you will love me very much for I am a very Great King."

"Dear Cousin," said Henry, "I never saw anyone I could love more than you, and to show how much I love you I have crossed the stormy seas to see you."

Then, having said those polite things to each other, the two Kings got off their horses, and arm-in-arm went in to dinner.

For three weeks after that there were Jolly Doings. There were parties and balls every day. There were tournaments in which the Kings fought against the Knights. And the Kings always won. There were fancy-dress balls, when all the Lords and Ladies dressed up and pretended to be someone else. That they thought was the greatest fun of all.

Everything about this meeting was so grand and glittering that it was called the Field of the Cloth of Gold. But "all that glitters is not gold," and it was all an idle Show. The French King got nothing out of it. For even before he went to meet Francis, Henry had been Plotting against him and after he got home he went on Plotting against him. A lot of the English Knights and Nobles too came home very Sad Men. For they had spent nearly all their money on grand clothes and rich jewels so as to make a Finer Show than the French Knights and Nobles. And all their lives after they had to be poor. So they got nothing out of it either. One wonders who did!

Henry VIII. Defender of the Faith

You remember that Wyclif had translated the Bible into English and that his followers went about telling people that they mustn't believe everything that the Pope told them. Now a Monk in Germany called Martin Luther began to say the same thing. Only he said Far More than Wyclif ever meant to say. He told the people of Germany that the Pope was a Bad Man and that they needn't believe anything that he told them at all. When Henry VIII heard about Martin Luther he was quite shocked. For although Henry was so Jolly and fond of Revelling, he was very pious and learned too. He could talk French and Latin like anything, and he thought that it was Dreadful not to believe everything the Pope told him to believe.

So now he wrote a book all in Latin saying what a Bad Man Martin Luther was and how wicked it was to say anything against the Pope.

He had the Book beautifully bound and made one of his Top Persons take it to the Pope "with the King of England's Compliments".

"Well now," said the Pope when he got this Handsome Present, "I think this is very Kind of my Dear Son Henry of England. I must give him Something in return." And after he had thought a bit he said, "I know. I'll give him a New Title. He'll like that. I'll call him Defender of the Faith."

Henry was as pleased as anything with his New Title. And all the people were pleased too to think that they had such a clever King who could write books.

A few years after this, however, Henry had a Dreadful Quarrel with his Friend the Pope. As Henry grew older he became more and more selfish and Autocratic.

Now Henry was tired of Queen Katherine and wanted a New Wife. So he asked the Pope, "Can I put away Katherine and have a New Wife?"

"No, indeed you can't," the Pope told him.

Again and again Henry tried to make the Pope say he could have a new wife. But the Pope just wouldn't say yes.

So at last Henry got Very Angry. "If you won't do as I ask you," he told the Pope, "I'll just do what I want without your leave. And I won't have you for Top Person of the English Church any more. I'll be the Top Person."

So Henry told all the people, "You needn't pay attention to the Pope any more and go asking him if you can do things or not. If you want to know what to do you can ask me. I'm Top of the English Church now, and it has nothing to do with the Pope. Now you must all say your prayers in English. That's all the difference there is."

Henry quarrelled with the Pope, but he kept the New Title the Pope had given him. Our Kings and Queens still keep it. If you look at a coin you will see FID: DEF: on it. That is short for the Latin which means, "Defender of the Faith".

Henry quarrelled with the Pope and he quarrelled with his great Chancellor because he thought it was Wolsey's fault that the Pope wouldn't let him marry a New Wife.

"You can go," he told him, "I don't want ever to see you again."

So poor Wolsey went away very sadly. For if he had loved himself and Power most, he had loved his King and his Country too. But he knew that although he had been Great, he hadn't really been Very Good. "If I had served God as Faithfully as I have served my King," he said, "He wouldn't have cast me off in my old age." Then he died.

Henry VIII and his Six Wives

Henry did as he wanted to and sent away poor Queen Katherine. He was very unkind to her in another way too. She had a daughter called Mary, who was quite a big girl by now. Katherine loved her daughter very much and Mary loved her Mother very much and wanted to go away with her. But Henry wouldn't let her. "No," he told her, "you stay here with me. You're not a Royal Princess any more. But you'll just stay here and do as I tell you."

As soon as he'd sent Queen Katherine away Henry married his new wife, who was called Anne Boleyn. She had a little daughter called Elizabeth, which pleased Henry very much. But he soon grew tired of Anne. So when people told him she was a Bad Lady he put her in Prison, and then cut off her head.

The very next day he married another Lady called Jane Seymour. She was Good and Gentle and it is a wonder she had the courage to marry the Blustering Bully that Henry had become. He was rather fat and ugly too by this time. For he ate and drank a lot and didn't play hard games of tennis or go in for sports any more.

But he liked Queen Jane very much, and when she had a little baby boy he just jumped for joy.

"Ho, ho!" he shouted. "Ho, ho! Now I have a son to be King of England when I'm dead. Was there ever anything so Grand."

He made a tremendous Fuss, and had the grandest of grand Christenings.

But before all the rejoicings were finished poor Queen Jane died. Henry was very sorry because he'd liked this wife best of all his wives. However he soon married another one. She was called Anne of Cleves. Henry had only seen a picture of her before she came to be married to him. In the picture she looked Quite Pretty. But she wasn't really pretty at all, and when Henry saw her he flew into a Dreadful Rage, and vowed that he wouldn't marry her.

His new Chancellor, however, told him, "You must marry her, or her German Friends will come and make a War about it."

"All right," said Henry. "I will." But to punish his Chancellor for making him do it he cut off his head.

Then Henry said to his new wife, "Look here, Anne, we don't get on a bit well together. I wish you'd go away and let me marry someone else. I'll give you a lot of money if you'll go."

"Thank you," said Anne, "I'll be very pleased to go."

So Anne went away; quite glad, very likely, to get away from such a bad-tempered man with her head still on her shoulders. She lived quite happily by herself, until she was a grey-haired old lady.

About a fortnight after Anne went away, Henry married another Lady called Catherine Howard. Very soon, however, he found out that she was a Bad Lady. So he cut off her head and the heads of a lot of her friends too.

Last of all Henry married Catherine Parr. She was a Good Woman and one wonders why she married such a Bad Man. Perhaps she was afraid that if she didn't marry Henry he would cut off her head At Once. But Catherine was clever as well as good, and she managed to keep her head on her shoulders.

When Henry first sat on the Throne he had heaps and heaps of money, so at first he didn't ask the people to give him any more. But with his Wild Ways he soon spent it all, and began asking for more. Then the People had to be taxed. They grumbled of course – and paid. Then they Rebelled and got killed. For Henry never minded how many heads he chopped off so long as he had his own way. So the reign which had begun with so much joy ended in misery.

In Henry VII's time the people had been happy and comfortable; by the end of Henry VIII's reign the land was full of beggars.

By the end of Henry VIII's reign England had become one of the top Nations among the Kingdoms of Europe. That was Wolsey's cleverness.

By the end of Henry VIII's reign England had far more ships than ever before. That was because the Merchant Adventurers wanted them, because Englishmen had become daring seamen and scoured the unknown seas in search of New Lands.

Henry VIII himself was a Bad, Selfish Bully. A Perfect Horror of a man. Yet the People never went hating him, and rebelling against him, as they did against Kings who weren't nearly as horrid.

The Childhood of a Prince

Tut-tut-ter-rut-tut went the trumpets. Rat-tat-a-tat-bang-bang went the drums. Ting-ting-ting-ding-dong, ting-ting-ting-ding-dong went the bells. Oh, what rejoicing in all the length and breadth of the land! For a little Prince had been born to stout, blustering King Henry VIII and his gentle Queen Jane.

And now the great little Prince must be Christened. What shall we call him? Henry, after his Father and Grandfather? No, no, no! He will be Prince of Wales. Edward of course. What better name for a Prince of Wales than Edward after the first Prince of Wales and the Black Prince?

As the Baby Prince grew into a little Boy he and his sister Elizabeth used to play a lot together. "Please can I do lessons with Edward?" asked Elizabeth, when Edward began to be taught. "I suppose you may," said his teacher, "but why a Princess wants to learn Greek and Latin, I'm sure I don't know."

So Edward and Elizabeth did lessons together. Edward had a whole lot of Masters, who taught him Greek and Latin, and Geography and Bible Stories, and ever so many other things. He was dreadfully clever and by the time he was eight he used to write his letters in Latin. We have some of them still, and some of his copybooks too. They are full of Greek and Latin exercises.

But although Edward just loved Doing Lessons he did other things too. He used to dance with Elizabeth and another little girl called Jane Dormer. He went riding and hunting too, and was very fond of all sorts of games and sports. And altogether he had a Very Jolly Time.

Edward VI. The Boy King

After a time little Prince Edward went to stay at Uncle Edward's Palace at Hertford. And there one winter's morning he was sitting quietly doing his lessons, when Uncle Edward arrived all hot and muddy, for he had ridden as fast as he could go from London.

"Put away your books," he said to Edward, "and get ready for a ride."

"Where are we going?" asked Edward when he was ready.

"Well, first of all we're going to see Elizabeth."

"Ah, good," said Edward. "I like Elizabeth."

So off they went, and when they got to Enfield, where Elizabeth was, Uncle Edward told them, "Your Father's dead, so now you are King Edward."

They both cried a bit, although they didn't really know their Father very well. But Edward was only nine and Elizabeth thirteen. So they couldn't help crying a little.

"Now that will do," said Uncle Edward. "You've cried quite enough. Remember you're a King now and you must come on to London and be crowned."

Edward VI was of course too young to do the Ruling. So Uncle Edward, Duke of Somerset did it. And all the old Troubles and Bothers about Kings' Uncles began over again, just like it was when Richard II was a boy. For Edward had another Uncle called Lord Seymour. He didn't see why Uncle Edward should have all the Power and tried hard to get some for himself. That was always the Bother with Kings' Uncles. They didn't Think of the Good-of-the-People, or of how to make them Happy and Comfortable. They only thought of making themselves Great. So of course the People began Rebelling.

And besides the old Bothers there were the new ones about what Church you belonged to. Edward VI belonged to the New English one, so did Uncle Edward and a lot more people. But a lot of other people, with Princess Mary at the Top of them, belonged to the Old Roman Church and still obeyed the Pope. And instead of leaving each other alone, and letting people Worship God quietly in the way they liked best, they fought and quarrelled about it. So Plottings, and Betrayings, and Beheadings began all over again.

Uncle Edward got a learned man called Cranmer to make the Prayer Book into English instead of Latin. He thought that would please everyone very much. But it only pleased some of them.

Others just hated it. The Cornish people especially hated it, for they still couldn't talk English. They still talked a language something like the Old British language. "We can't understand this new Prayer Book," they said.

"But you must use it. It's the Law now," they were told.

"Well we just won't, so there," they said, and they started Rebelling. That didn't do any Good. For Uncle Edward sent a whole lot of soldiers to stop them and ever so many of them got killed.

All over England people began Rebelling about one thing or another.

All this time King Edward had been going on with his lessons like a good little boy. He had never had the chance of being a Real King with his Uncle doing the Ruling. And Uncle Edward got more and more Haughty and carried on just as if he were the King.

All the time too Uncle Seymour and Uncle Edward were quarrelling, and Uncle Seymour was always trying to curry favour with the King. He found out that Uncle Edward kept him very short of Pocket Money. So he used to send Pocket Money to King Edward on the sly. "Spend that on anything you like," he would say. "When it's done I'll give you more. It's a shame how Uncle Edward treats you. Why don't you begin to do the Ruling by yourself? You're growing into a big boy now. It's quite time you were allowed to do some Ruling."

At last Uncle Edward got tired of Uncle Seymour's Plotting. So he put him in Prison and then cut off his head.

When he had done that Uncle Edward thought that he'd got rid of his worst enemy and that now he could do what he liked. But he soon found out that he'd made a lot more enemies, for a lot of the Top Lords were shocked at him for what he had done. "Fancy cutting off your own brother's head," they said. "Such a man is not fit to Rule." So they began Plotting against him. And at last he found himself in Prison and soon his head was chopped off too.

Then the Duke of Northumberland, another sort of King's Uncle, did the Ruling. He was even more Haughty and greedy than the Duke of Somerset had been, and soon he too began Plotting.

"Who's going to reign after you?" he asked the King one day.

"I suppose my sister Mary comes next," said Edward. "My Father said she was to."

"Well that will be rather dreadful," said Northumberland. "You know she's very fond of the Pope. She'll make friends with him again. Your Father wouldn't have liked that to happen."

"No, he wouldn't. Neither would we. But what can we do?"

"You can make a will and leave the Throne to Lady Jane Grey. She's the Great-granddaughter of Henry VII. So she's got a very good Right to be Queen. She's a very fine Lady too. I ought to know for she's married to my son."

So Edward made his Will and soon afterwards he died. He was only fifteen and had never really done any Ruling and he wasn't to blame for the bad things that happened during his reign.

The Worth-While thing to remember about it is that a lot of Schools were built. They were called King Edward Schools. We still have a lot of them. One of the most Famous is Christ's Hospital. We generally call it The Blue Coat School and the pupils who go to it still wear yellow stockings and long blue coats just as they did in Edward VI's time.

Lady Jane Grey. A Ten Days' Queen

Now," said John, Duke of Northumberland to himself, as soon as Edward VI was dead, "now I can make myself Great. For of course Jane will do anything I tell her to. She's only a girl and even if she can talk Greek and Latin and Hebrew, she doesn't know anything about Ruling."

So off he went to tell Lady Jane that she was Queen now. He thought that she would be very pleased. But she wasn't. Instead of clapping her hands with joy, she began to cry. "Oh, I can't be Queen," she sobbed. "I don't know anything about Ruling. I can't do it."

"Come, come," said Northumberland, "don't carry on like a silly girl. It's your Duty. Your Cousin wanted you to be Queen, or he wouldn't have said so in his Will. Put on your best clothes and we'll go for a ride through London. Think how grand you'll be having everybody cheering you and shouting God save the Queen."

"Well, if it's my Duty, I suppose I must do it," said Jane. So she dried her eyes and put on her grandest dress and rode to the Tower of London with the Duke of Northumberland.

But not one cheer did she get. No one shouted, "God save the Queen". The People just looked at her in silence and mumbled to themselves. "What's all this?" they asked. "That's not old Harry's daughter. We don't want any Queen Jane. We want Princess Mary."

So they turned their backs to poor Queen Jane. When Princess Mary heard of these Goings-On she was Very Angry. "If Cousin Jane thinks I'm going to sit still and let her steal my Crown she's very much mistaken," she said.

So she gathered all her Faithful Followers and began marching to London. And everywhere she passed the people cheered and shouted, "God save Queen Mary!"

Duke John hadn't expected that at all. "Dear me," he said to himself. "I suppose I'll have to fight for the Crown."

So he went to Jane's Father and told him, "I'll have to go and find some soldiers. I'm leaving you here to look after Jane when I'm away. And whatever you do, don't let that Mary get in here. If you do it's All Up."

Then Duke John went off to get some soldiers. But he found it wasn't so easy as he'd thought it would be. All the Top Nobles said, "Oh no, thank you. We don't want your Jane. We'd much rather have Henry's daughter, Mary. The Throne's really hers by Right you know."

Then when they saw how things were going, even the Nobles who had joined Duke John went off and joined Mary. So soon the Duke found that he had hardly any army at all while Mary's army was growing bigger and bigger.

When Jane's Father heard all the people shouting, "Queen Mary!" he got frightened. "Oh dear, oh dear," he thought, "I wish John hadn't left me here all alone to look after Jane. What am I to do? I'd better lock the gates."

So he locked the gates. But soon a lot of Mary's friends came hammering at them. "Let us in," they shouted.

"Give us the keys. This is Queen Mary's Town House. She'll be here soon. You'd better let us in."

So at last, trembling with fear, Jane's Father opened the Gates. Then as fast as he could he ran to Jane's room.

"Jane, my dear," he told her, "I'm afraid you're not Queen any longer. Everyone is shouting, "God save Queen Mary". And I've had to let them in."

"Oh, Father, I'm so glad," said Jane. "That's the best News I've heard since you told me I must be Queen. Please can I go home now?"

But poor Jane found that it wasn't so easy as all that. She had come to the Tower as a Queen and now she had to stay there as a Prisoner.

When Duke John heard that Mary's friends had got into the Tower he knew that he had lost. He had hardly any soldiers so he couldn't fight. Only one thing was left for him to do, so he did it.

He too threw his cap in the air and shouted, "God save Queen Mary!" But he was a little too late in doing that. Queen Mary's friends just took him prisoner and marched him off to the Tower.

"He's a Very Bad Dangerous Man," they said. "He'd much better have his head chopped off." And chopped off it was.

"And what about Lady Jane?" they asked.

"Oh, well," said Mary, "it wasn't really her fault. It was just that Bad Man Duke John who led her on. So I won't cut her head off. But she'll have to stay in Prison and her Husband and Father too."

So that was the end of poor Lady Jane's reign. It had lasted just ten days.

Mary I. A Very Sad Time

All the people sang for joy when Mary became Queen. But before long a lot of them began to be very Sorry. They soon found out that she didn't care much about the Good-of-the-People and just wanted to have her own way about everything.

"I'm going to marry the King of Spain," she told them.

"Oh, don't do that," they said. "Couldn't you marry an Englishman?"

"An Englishman! What Englishman is my Equal I should like to know?" said Mary. "You surely don't expect me to marry a Subject!"

Seeing that Mary was quite determined to marry Philip of Spain a lot of the Nobles began a Plot to get rid of her. "Anything would be better than having a Proud Spaniard lording it over us and calling himself King of England," they said.

"Let's try Lady Jane Grey again," said some.

"Or the Princess Elizabeth," said others.

Then they gathered all their Faithful Followers and began fighting Mary. But they got beaten and all the Top Nobles who were in the Plot had their heads cut off. And poor little Lady Jane who had never wanted to Rule got all the blame. So she, and her Husband, and Father, and Brother all lost their Heads too.

After all these cruel Beheadings the people began to be afraid of Mary. So she got her own way and married Philip of Spain. He came from Spain and rode through London with a lot of Pomp and Splendour. He brought boxes and boxes full of gold with him and gave people grand presents. But in spite of that no one liked him except Mary. She loved him ever such a lot and did everything she could to please him.

One of the first things she did was to make friends with the Pope.

The Pope wouldn't of course come to England himself, but he sent one of his Top Persons. Philip and Mary knelt down before him and told him, "King Henry VIII did a very wicked thing when he quarrelled with the Pope. We and all the people of England are Very Sorry. Please forgive us."

"In the Pope's name I forgive you," said the Messenger. "Now all the People of England belong to the Holy Catholic Church."

But it needed more than a few words from King, Queen and Pope to make England Roman Catholic again. The People who belonged to the New English Church and the Protestants wouldn't stop going to their Churches. Mary was determined that they should. So the most terrible time of her reign began.

"I belong to the Roman Catholic Church and all my People must belong to it too," said Mary. "If they don't do as I tell them they must be punished."

So the people who wouldn't do as Mary told them were fined and imprisoned, and when that didn't make them do what they were told they were killed. They were killed in the most horrid and cruel way by being put on to bonfires and burnt up.

Then Philip got tired of living in England, where everyone hated him, and he went back to Spain. That made Mary very unhappy, for she loved her husband, although no one else did.

He only came back once and that was to get money to help him in a War he was starting against France. Very unwillingly Parliament gave him the money he asked for and so got rid of him. But the War ended sadly for Mary. For the French besieged and took Calais, which had belonged to the English ever since the days of Edward I.

She thought that Calais was one of the most important parts of her Kingdom and that it was a dreadful disgrace to lose it. That made Mary still more unhappy. "When I am dead," she said, "you will find Calais written on my heart."

And very soon afterward, unhappy and unloved and lonely, she died.

Elizabeth. The Clouds Roll Away

While Queen Mary was going on in her Dangerous Fashion, her sister Princess Elizabeth was living at Hatfield. Being at Hatfield was rather like being in Prison. For Mary had sent Elizabeth there, and told her, "Now you just stay there until I say you may leave. And don't let me hear of you trying to mix yourself up with the Ruling, or trying to make yourself Queen, or anything of that sort. If you do it will be the worse for you."

So Elizabeth kept as quiet as a mouse, hoping that Mary would forget about her. For she didn't want to be made into a bonfire, or have her head chopped off. But she found it very dull, for Elizabeth was a Jolly Lady who liked dancing and parties and having people saying nice things to her.

Then one grey November day she had been for a walk in the Park and sat down under a Great Oak tree to rest. And as she sat there Elizabeth saw some Very Grand Gentlemen coming towards her.

When the Gentlemen were quite close Elizabeth saw that they were very grave but not stern. So she smiled at them, and they took off their hats very politely and bowed low. "We have come to tell you," they said, "that Queen Mary is dead. Please will you come to London and be our Queen?"

"Oh, how wonderful!" said Elizabeth, clasping her hands. Then, being very learned, like all the Tudor Ladies, she knelt down on the damp grass and said her prayers in Latin.

So Elizabeth set out for London with a great procession of Knights and Nobles and soldiers and servants. All along the way the people cheered her as she passed, and Elizabeth bowed and smiled and waved her hand and was as happy as could be.

On and on they went until they came to the Tower of London. When the Procession came to the great gate Elizabeth stopped and spoke to the People. "Last time I was here," she said, "I was made to go in by the Traitors' Gate, although I never was a Traitor. Now I come as Queen. Now I can go in by the Great Gate of my own Free Will. See how kind God has been to me. I too must try to be kind to all my People."

To be Kind to everybody wasn't at all an easy Job. Some hoped that Elizabeth would make friends with the Pope and tell all the people that they must go to the Roman Catholic Church just as Mary had done. But most of them hoped that she would say that everyone must go to the New English Church. And that was what she did. And although she was rather unkind to the Catholic Fathers and Priests, she wasn't nearly as unkind as Mary had been to the English Church Clergymen. So things began to be much more Comfortable. People felt that the horrid black cloud had rolled away and they began to be merry and bright again. Elizabeth was such a nice change after Mary that the People just loved her. They gave her pet names like Good Queen Bess and Gloriana. That shows how fond they were of her.

She was very Clever and she thought that she was very pretty too. She wasn't really pretty, but she used to wear lovely dresses and lots of jewellery, and she always looked very grand.

Lots of people wanted to marry her. Great Kings and Princes used to send and say, "Please will you marry me?" Even the King of Spain, who had been married to her sister Mary, asked her. To them all she said, "Thank you very much. It's most kind of you. I'll think about it." Then after a bit she told them, "No, thank you, I don't want to marry you. I'd rather be Queen of England all by myself and have my People loving me." So she never married at all.

Lots of Englishmen too wanted to marry her – Ordinary Gentlemen as well as Dukes and Lords. But Elizabeth was really too Proud to marry a Subject. All the same she liked to have them loving her and wanting to marry her. And when they left off doing it and married some other Lady she was very much annoyed. So she would put them in Prison for a bit to teach them better Manners.

Elizabeth. About a Very Unhappy Queen

When Elizabeth was sitting on the Throne of England there was a Queen in Scotland too. She was called Mary, Queen of Scots, and she and Elizabeth were cousins.

Mary, Queen of Scots was younger than Elizabeth and very beautiful as well as clever. She had really been Queen of Scotland ever since she was a tiny baby. But she had lived all her life in France. There she married the King of France and only went to Scotland to do the Ruling when he died.

When Mary of England died, Mary, Queen of Scots thought that she should have been made Queen of England. So she called herself Queen of Scotland, France and England. Of course that made Elizabeth very angry, although it was no worse than Elizabeth calling herself Queen of England and France, when she didn't rule over one little bit of France.

In spite of this the Cousins pretended to be Great Friends and used to write loving letters to each other.

Mary was only nineteen when she came back to Scotland to do the Ruling, and she soon found that the Throne of Scotland was a very Uncomfortable Seat.

The New Scottish Church was much more Strict and Stern than the English one. They did away with Bishops and called their Clergy Ministers. They thought it was wicked to kneel or read prayers out of a Book. So when they prayed the people stood up and listened to the Minister while he talked to God out of his own head.

Mary, Queen of Scots was a Roman Catholic and when she came to do the Ruling in Scotland she wished to go on being one. She didn't want to make all the people go to her Church, but she wanted to be allowed to go to it herself. However, the Scots thought that was very wicked of her and tried to make her give it up.

After a bit Mary married a New Husband called Darnley. He wasn't really a very Nice Man and one day he got killed. A lot of people thought that Mary had killed him, or at least that it was Mary's fault that he got killed. So things got worse and worse and at last there was Civil War.

Mary's army got dreadfully beaten and poor Mary didn't know what to do or where to go. She was sure that the people would put her in Prison if she stayed in Scotland, so she said to herself, "I'll go and pay Cousin Elizabeth a visit. Surely she'll be kind to me when she knows how dreadfully unhappy I have been."

But when Elizabeth got the letter she wasn't a bit pleased. She had never seen Cousin Mary, but she knew that she was young and pretty. The Top Nobles might go loving her and wanting to marry her when they ought not to want to marry anyone but herself. Besides that, Elizabeth had never forgiven Mary for calling herself Queen of England. She mightn't stop at just calling herself Queen of England. She might want to be it. "Oh no," thought Elizabeth, "I certainly can't have a visitor like that."

So she wrote and told Mary, "No, I can't have you. A lot of people think it was your fault that your husband got killed. And until everybody says it wasn't your fault I can't have you for a visit. So just stay where you are."

When Mary saw that Cousin Elizabeth wasn't going to be kind to her she wanted to go away again.

But Elizabeth wouldn't let her go. She kept her in England, not as a Guest but as a Prisoner.

That made a lot of people angry with Elizabeth and very sorry for Mary, and they were always plotting to try and set her free. But they never could do it.

At last some very daring people got up a Plot to kill Elizabeth and put Mary on the Throne. And when Elizabeth's Top People found out about it they were very angry, and frightened too.

"Look here," they said to Elizabeth, "it's really Too Dangerous your keeping that Cousin of yours in Prison. It would be much better to cut off her head. Then nobody could go wanting to make her Queen."

"Oh no," said Elizabeth, "I could never do that."

But the Top Persons talked and talked, and at last Elizabeth said, "Very well, have it your own way." And she signed the paper which said that Mary's head was to be cut off.

As soon as they'd got the paper some of the Top Nobles hurried off and chopped off poor Mary's head. But when Elizabeth heard about it she was Very Angry. Then she cried and cried and put on mourning. "I never meant you to go and do it," she said. "I only

signed that paper to make you stop bothering me." So to punish
them she put one of the Top Persons in Prison and made him
pay ever such a lot of money as a fine for having done what he
was told to do.

Elizabeth. The Navy that Couldn't be Beaten

Elizabeth was a very Clever Lady and she did the Ruling
well. She had a whole lot of Clever Men too who helped
her. They saw that the best way to make themselves Great was to
make England Peaceful.

So the Top Noblemen gave up building great strong Castles
with little slits of windows for firing guns out of, and ditches full
of water round them to keep the enemy out. Instead they built
comfortable houses
with big windows
and lovely gardens
round them. They felt
that they could
do that Quite
Safely, for they
didn't expect
any Foreign
Foe to be coming
at them.

Except for the Bothers about Mary Queen of Scots there were
hardly any Rebellings while Elizabeth sat on the Throne. She
didn't want to go Conquering other Countries. She knew that
wasn't any use. All the same she did send Armies every Now and
Again when she wanted to help her Friends. But she did it on
the sly.

King Philip of Spain was the Top King in Europe. He ruled over Portugal and the countries we call Holland and Belgium now as well as Spain. He was very Rich too. For his daring Sailors had discovered America, where they found lots of gold and Treasure, and they brought whole Shiploads home to Spain.

Now King Philip began a dreadful War trying to make all his People go to his Church. And as nearly all the People in Holland and Belgium were Protestants they had a terrible time. So Elizabeth sent Soldiers to help them too. She helped them quite a lot. But of course she wasn't fighting against the King of Spain. Oh dear, no!

All the same the King of Spain knew what Elizabeth was doing and he got very angry. He was very angry with the English Sailors too. For the English Sailors, like the Spanish Sailors, were always scouring the Seas looking for Treasure and Adventures. Sometimes they met. Sometimes they fought. Sometimes the English beat the Spaniards and brought home to England all the gold and Treasure that the Spaniards had been taking to Spain.

The most daring of these Seamen was Francis Drake, and King Philip at last complained about him to Elizabeth. "He's a most Impudent Pirate," he told her. "Oh, my dear Brother," said Elizabeth, "I assure you I know nothing about it. And if I catch the Rascal I promise you he shall be suitably punished."

But she took a big share of the Treasure which Drake brought home, and she went and had dinner with him on board his Famous Ship, the *Golden Hind*.

"You know the King of Spain says you are an Impudent Pirate," she told Drake severely. Then after dinner she asked for a sword, and when it was brought she looked sternly at Drake. "Kneel down, Pirate," she said. And when Drake knelt down before her, instead of cutting off his head, she gave him a good hard smack on the shoulder and said, "Rise, Sir Francis."

So that was the way the Rascal was punished. Elizabeth made him an Admiral too, and he went on scouring the Seas and attacking the Spaniards as hard as ever.

"I won't stand this sort of thing any more," cried Philip, "I shall go and Conquer these English and teach them a lesson."

So he began to gather Soldiers and Sailors and guns and ships. "Ho, ho!" said Drake, when he heard about it. "We must put a stop to that." So he set out for Spain, and as Bold as Brass sailed into the Harbour where all Philip's Ships were gathered. He sank or set fire to most of them and sailed away again. "Ha, ha!" he said. "I've singed the King of Spain's Beard for him."

Philip was Furious. But he set to work and got more Ships built, and in a year he was ready to go Conquering England. So one May Morning a hundred and twenty-nine ships sailed out from Spain. Philip called this great fleet the Invincible Armada, which means, "The Navy which Cannot be Conquered".

At first the English didn't believe that Philip would dare to come trying to conquer them. But when they saw he really meant it they were furious. "Coming to Conquer us?" they cried. "We'll see about that."

All over the Country people gathered, till there were three great Armies waiting for
the Spaniards when they came.

On Sea it was the same. The Queen had only a few ships, and none of them as big as the Spanish ones. But all the Merchant Adventurers gave their Ships. All the big towns got money together and built ships. "Mr Mayor," said Elizabeth, "London will be expected to give fifteen Ships."

"Fifteen ships!" said the Lord Mayor of London. "Fifteen ships indeed! London will give thirty ships."

And so it went on. All over England there was Hurry and Bustle; Men being drilled, ships being built, food being gathered. But at last everything was ready. Everything was ready except the enemy. There were no Spaniards.

But the army stayed together and the Ships stayed waiting at Plymouth and everybody kept watching and watching for the Spaniards to come.

At last one July day when Drake and some more Top Sailors were playing bowls they heard a cry, "The Spaniards, the Spaniards!" They stopped their game and looked out to sea. Yes, sure enough, there they were at last.

"Oh, but they're big," said the Sailors. "And what a lot."

"Oh, well," said Drake, "let's finish our game. There will be plenty of time to beat the Spaniards afterwards."

So they finished their game and then sailed away to meet the Foe.

For a whole week they fought, and the English always had the best of it. For their little Ships moved about far more easily than the great big handsome Spanish ones. And of course the English Sailors knew all the coast far better than the Spaniards did.

Then a terrible storm came on and that did for the Spanish ships. The wind just blew and blew and drove them away. It drove them away up to the North of Scotland and down again past Ireland. They got dashed on to rocks and smashed to pieces. The wind tore the sails and broke the masts, and at last only about fifty broken up, half-wrecked ships reached Spain.

England was saved.

Elizabeth. "The World is so Full of a Number of Things"

Years went by and the People felt Safe and Comfortable and not afraid of any Conquering people coming at them. Daring Sailors sailed the seas, finding new Lands and claiming them for the Queen of England. They came home with wonderful stories of all they had seen in those Far Countries. They brought Strange Things home with them too. They brought Potatoes, which people planted in their gardens and found that they were very nice to eat with their Good Roast Beef.

They brought Tobacco. Oh, how funny it was to see the gentlemen sitting with long tubes in their mouths puffing out smoke. And the smell of it! Some people liked it. Most of the Ladies didn't. "Pooff!" they said, "if you want to smoke that Horrid Stuff go out into the garden. I won't allow it in my drawing-room."

They brought birds with bright green feathers – birds that talked. They said, "Poor Polly, Pretty Polly," and lots of other things.

There seemed no end to the Strange Things these Far Travellers brought home. Every day it seemed as if they brought something new. It was a wonderful time to be alive in.

There was the Theatre too. If you lived in London you could go to the wonderful new Theatre called "The Globe" and see

the plays of Master William Shakespeare being acted. At least
Gentlemen could go. It wasn't proper for Ladies. However, some
of the Daring Ones did go. But they put black masks on to cover
their faces, so that no one should know who they were.

Oh yes, it was a Wonderful Time to be alive in. You could Do
Something and Hear Something Interesting every day. And
in the evening, when the candles were lit and the fire burning
brightly, you could sit and listen while someone read lovely
poetry like Spenser's *Faerie Queene*. Or perhaps it would be
something graver, like an Essay by Sir Francis Bacon, or a chapter
out of Sir Philip Sidney's *Arcadia*. There were such a lot of Books
to choose from.

Yes, life was Interesting and Safe and Comfortable.

But the Queen was growing old.

The Queen was growing Very Old. She had loved to dance.
Now she couldn't dance any more. She just sat still staring at
nothing with her finger in her mouth.

The Queen was very ill. But she wouldn't go to bed. She had
always done exactly as she liked, and she meant to go on doing
exactly as she liked. So she lay on the floor with cushions all
about her.

But in the end she let herself be put to bed. Then for the last
time some of the Top Nobles came to see her.

"Do you want your Cousin the King of Scotland to be King of
England?" they asked.

She seemed to say, "Yes."

Then the Great Queen died.

The People wept for her as they had never done before. For
there had never been so Great a Queen.

She had scolded and petted her People by turns, but frowning or smiling she had loved them. She had hated and cheated her Enemies, but she had been True and Kindly to her Friends.
She had been vain and stingy, generous and noble, by turns. But whatever she did, whatever she was, she had loved her People, she had loved her England.

James I of England, VI of Scotland.
The Story of Guy Fawkes

For hundreds of Years, ever since Edward I's times, the Kings of England had gone Conquering in Scotland, wanting to join England and Scotland together. Now it happened quite easily. James VI of Scotland just came and sat on the Throne and was called James I of England. What a lot of Bothers and Hatings it would have saved if only those old Kings hadn't been so Impatient.

James was the son of Poor Mary Queen of Scots who had been kept such a long time in Prison and then had her head cut off. He had been King of Scotland for years and years before he came to be King of England too. Of course when he was a small boy he didn't do the Ruling. That was done by some of the Top Nobles just as it used to be in England when there was a Boy-King. And it was done even worse than they used to do it.

Even after James Grew Up he let the Top Nobles do the Ruling pretty much, for he really didn't care about it. He was too lazy. He was clever in a kind of way, for his tutor had been a very learned man. But he didn't teach the King the sort of things that would be useful to him as a King. So James could write books and talk Greek but wasn't much good at Ruling.

His manners weren't nice either. For he'd had no Mother when he was little to look after him and see that he put on his clothes tidily, and there had been no one even to tell him to wash properly – "Well behind the ears Remember, and see that your nails are clean," and that sort of thing. So his nails never were clean.

However, most of the English thought he would do well enough, especially after they'd trained him a bit. The Roman Catholics were quite pleased, for they said, "Surely for the Sake of his Poor Dear Mother he'll be kinder to us than that Elizabeth was." But James had been brought up to the strict New Scottish Church and the Roman Catholics soon found out that he wasn't going to be a bit kind to them.

That made them angry, so they started doing some Plotting and Rebelling. However, that didn't do them any good. Some of them had their heads chopped off and some of them landed in Prison. So they got more angry still, and a few very Bad Ones started a Big Plot.

They decided to kill the King and all the Top Persons in the Country. But how were they to do it? There weren't enough of them to make a Civil War. They knew they'd be beaten in no time. So they talked and talked and at last they thought of a Plan.

"We'll wait until Parliament is sitting," they said. "The King and all the Top Persons will be gathered together in the Parliament House. Then we'll blow them all up with Gunpowder."

"But how can we blow them up?"

"Quite easily. There are cellars under the Parliament House. They're let to People to store Things in. We'll rent one. We'll fill it full of Barrels of Gunpowder. Then when the King and all the Top Persons are in, all we have to do is to set a light to the Gunpowder, and the thing's done."

"But suppose somebody sees the Barrels and asks questions?"

"It's not likely. But to make it Quite Safe we can cover them up with a lot of sticks and firewood."

So they began gathering barrels of Gunpowder and sticks and wood and putting them into the cellar under the Parliament House until they'd got enough.

"Now we're ready," they said. "When does Parliament meet?"

"The fifth of November."

"Ah, that's quite soon now! Let's settle who is to set fire to the Gunpowder. Shall we Cast Lots?"

"No," said Guy Fawkes, "I'll do it."

So it was all arranged, and the Plotters were very joyful, for they didn't see how anything could Go Wrong now.

But one of them had a Friend that he loved Very Much. He knew that this Friend would be going to the Opening of Parliament, and he just couldn't bear to think of him being Blown Up.

So the Plotter wrote to his Friend and told him, "This is to warn you not to go to Parliament. Go away into the Country where you will be Safe. Because all these wicked People are going to get a Terrible Blow. But they won't see who gives it."

When the Friend got this letter he didn't know what to do. "It sounds very Dangerous and Important," he said to himself. "I'd better show it to some Top Person."

So he took it to a Top Nobleman, who took it to the King.

"Ah!" said the King when he'd read it. "Parliament is to get a Terrible Blow but won't see who gives it. That must be Gunpowder. You'd better have a good look round and see if you can find any Gunpowder about."

So at Midnight on the 4th November a lot of men with Drawn Swords in their hands went searching the cellars under the Parliament House. They crept about and crept about and couldn't find anything. But at last in a dark corner they saw Guy Fawkes. He tried to get away, but they were too quick for him and they caught him.

In his pockets they found Things for lighting fires with. Beneath the firewood and sticks they found the Gunpowder. Guy Fawkes saw it wasn't any good saying that he wasn't doing any Harm or that he was just having a Look Round or something like that. So he owned up.

The Gunpowder Plot had failed. And instead of doing good to the Roman Catholics it did a lot of harm. Only a few Bad

Ones had been in this Plot. But even the Quite Good Ones, who would never have done anything so wicked as kill the King and all the Top Persons, were made to suffer because of it. They were all unkindly treated and life became very hard for them.

At first when he came, James let the Top Nobles who had helped Queen Elizabeth to rule go on doing it. So Things went on pretty well. But when they died he chose rather Bad Men for his Top Persons. He didn't choose them because they were Wise or because they knew anything about Ruling. He chose them because they were Nice-Looking and had Wheedling Ways. And as James was very fond of them he let them do as they liked and gave them all sorts of titles and heaps of money too.

In this way James spent such a lot that he was always asking Parliament for more money. And of course that meant that he was always quarrelling with Parliament.

For when Parliament wouldn't give him as much money as he wanted he got angry. "The King can't do Anything Wrong," he said. "The King is Always Right. So what you have to do is to Obey him."

"Oh no," said Parliament, "we must do what we think is Right."

"Very Well," said James, "if that's the way you are going to carry on I don't want you. You can go home."

So all the members went home, and for ten years there wasn't any Parliament at all.

Then James tried to get money in other ways, and that meant more quarrelling.

The Quarrels weren't very Bad Ones. They never got to Rebelling and Fighting. It just was that King and People didn't get on together and when James died no one was Very Sorry.

Charles I. A Lot of Bother with Parliament

Charles, Prince of Wales now became King. James had always told him, "Now remember, the King can do no Wrong." So Charles started off being autocratic. But that wasn't any good. For in its Tussles with James, Parliament had found out how Strong it was, so they said, "Oh no, we don't believe all that Nonsense about the "King can do no Wrong". If he doesn't do what we want him to, that's Wrong. If he doesn't know what's for the Good-of-the-People, we do."

So poor Charles soon found out that they were going to be Very Tiresome. And the worst of it was that everyone didn't want the Same Thing.

By this time Everything had got Mixed up with Religion and with what Church people wanted to go to. Besides the English Church and Roman Church, a new Church had been getting quite Common. The people who went to it were called Puritans.

They didn't want to have Bishops or a Prayer Book or altars or beautiful Churches. They wanted to have everything as plain as could be. It wasn't only in Church that they wanted things to be plain.

In those days men used to wear bright-coloured Clothes made of silk and velvet. They wore big lace collars and hats with feathers in them, and their hair was long and curled just like a girl's.

The Puritans thought all that was wicked. So they wore dark clothes and plain linen collars, and cut their hair short. They spoke slowly and sadly and hardly ever smiled.

Then being a Puritan or not being a Puritan got all mixed up with the Ruling. So after a time if you wore sad clothes and had short hair you were thought to be an Enemy of the King. If you wore long curly hair and gay clothes you were thought to be an Enemy of the People. It was all very Difficult and Confusing.

Charles I. The Great Rebellion

The quarrels got worse and worse until at last it came to Civil War – you know what kind of war that is. The Scots and the Irish all joined in too. So it was called the Great Rebellion.

The King and the Lords were on one side, the Parliament and Puritans on the other. Those on the King's side were called Cavaliers because a lot of them rode on horses. Those on the Parliament side were called Roundheads because they had short hair instead of long curls like the Cavaliers.

The Top Person on the Roundhead side was Oliver Cromwell. He wasn't a Real Soldier, but just a Gentleman Farmer sort of person. Indeed there were very few real soldiers, especially on the Parliament side. But Oliver knew how to make people Obey.

So he got a whole lot of men together and drilled them and drilled them, till he made them so Strong that they were called Cromwell's Ironsides.

This war went on for four years. At first the King's side won a good deal. But when Oliver got going with his Ironsides the Puritans began to win most. At last at a Battle called Naseby the Cavaliers got dreadfully beaten.

For a little time after that the War went on, but the Cavaliers always got beaten and at last Charles gave up all hope. He didn't know what to do, so at length he thought he'd give himself up to the Scots. "After all," he said to himself, "they are my Own People. Perhaps they would be kinder to me than the English have been."

But Charles was at Oxford and the Scottish Camp was at Newark. And how was he to get there with the country in between swarming with Roundhead Soldiers? It was very Difficult and Dangerous.

But one day two gentlemen rode quietly out of Oxford. A servant rode behind with the luggage. The Servant was King Charles. No one took any notice of them so they got safely to Newark.

"This is quite a surprise, Your Majesty," said the Scottish General when he saw Charles; "we didn't expect you."

"Well," said Charles, "I thought if I came and talked to you we might settle things up."

They talked and talked but it was no good. For the Scots wanted Charles to promise a whole lot of things that he couldn't or wouldn't promise.

Then the Scottish General told the Parliament, "The King is here, but he won't do anything we ask him to. You can have him

if you like." So the Parliament people came and took Charles
Prisoner.

As soon as Charles was a Prisoner the Parliament told
the Soldiers, "We don't need you any more now. You can all
go home."

But the Soldiers said, "We'll do nothing of the Kind. We
haven't been paid for ever so long. We want our money first."

For the Soldiers knew how strong they had become. It was they
who really ruled the Country now and they made up their minds
to get still more power.

They thought it would be a Good Idea to get hold of the King
and take him away from the Parliament.

So one evening a man called Cornet Joyce, with a whole lot of
Soldiers behind him, rode up to the house where Charles was
being kept a Prisoner. He left his Soldiers at the door and walked
right into the King's room.

"Your Majesty," he said, "I've
come to take you away."

"Oh!" said Charles.
"Where do you want to
take me?"

"Well, we think
you'd be more
comfortable with
the Army than
here."

"But it's very
late. Much too late
to start off on a
journey."

"All right," said Joyce, "I'll wait till morning, but you'd better make up your mind to come with me then."

So next morning when Charles came downstairs he saw the whole Courtyard filled with Soldiers all mounted and ready to start.

Charles looked at the horse all ready saddled for him. He was very fond of riding and very good at it. It would be nice to go for a ride. So at length he said, "All right. I'll come with you."

And in this way Charles became the Prisoner of the Army instead of being the Prisoner of the Parliament.

Charles was much more comfortable with the Army than he had been with the Parliament. They gave him Hampton Court to live in, where he could do pretty much what he liked. Still he was a Prisoner and he got rather tired of being one. So one day he ran away to the Isle of Wight. He thought that he was going to friends and that he would be free there. But he'd made a mistake and soon found that he had really come to a worse Prison.

Meanwhile the Parliament and the Army went on quarrelling. But Cromwell was Top Person in the Army and he meant to be Top Person in the Parliament too. So one day a man called Colonel Pride came with a whole lot of soldiers and posted them all round the House of Commons. As the Members arrived each one who wouldn't promise to do exactly what Cromwell wanted was seized and made prisoner. When they were finished there were only about fifty Members left. This was still the Long Parliament, but people called it the Rump, because it was only a bit of a Parliament.

After this Cromwell was Top Person in the Army and Top Person in the Parliament. But even he couldn't always keep the Army in order. Now some of the Fiercest of the Soldiers began to say that Charles was too Bad a Man to be allowed to live and he ought to die for all his Wicked Deeds.

Cromwell had never meant to kill Charles. He didn't want to do it now. But he saw that if he was to go on being Top Person and Soldiers' Favourite he'd have to do it.

So Charles was brought to London and a lot of people got together to be his Judges. They didn't quite know what to say he'd done. So they said he'd done High Treason. But High Treason meant doing something Bad against the King. So they just invented a New Crime and called it High Treason against the Nation. They said Charles had no Business to make War against the Parliament, and that he was a Tyrant, a Traitor and a Murderer, and that he must die.

So poor Charles had his head cut off.

Charles wasn't really a Bad Man. He was Obstinate and Tricky, and you couldn't trust him. He hadn't been a Good King. It would have needed a Very Wise Man to be a Good King at such a Difficult Time. And Charles wasn't Very Wise. But when he came to die he behaved in such a Kingly way that even his enemies had to admire him.

CHAPTER XII · THE COMMONWEALTH

As soon as Charles was dead Parliament said that Kings were bad and useless and that England would have no more of them. They said that England and Scotland and Ireland were to be called a Commonwealth and that everyone was to be equal. Lords were bad and useless too, they said. So they did away with the House of Lords.

But when the Scots heard of all these Goings-On they were Very Angry.

"We don't want to be a Commonwealth," said the Scots, "and have Cromwell and his Ironsides Lording it over us. We like to have a King. And we'll have one too."

So they sent to Charles the Prince of Wales and told him, "We want you to come and be our King." He came, and was crowned at Scone, where all the Scottish Kings used to be crowned, and was called Charles II.

When Cromwell heard what the Scots had done he was Very Angry. "I'll soon put a stop to that," he said.

But the Irish too began Rebelling. "I'll just put a stop to that first," said Cromwell. And off he went to Ireland with his Ironsides.

Up and down the Country he went Rampaging like a Fury, doing the most horrid cruel killings and slayings, till the Irish hated and loathed his name. Then he set out for Scotland and went Conquering the Scots in battle after battle.

But while Cromwell was busy doing his Conquering in Scotland the young King said to himself, "Now that Cromwell is so busy here I think it would be a Good Idea if I went to England and got the English to make me their King too." So with a little Army he went off as fast as he could to England.

When Cromwell heard about it he was very much astonished. "I can't allow this," he said. So he hurried after Charles as fast as he could.

The two armies met near Worcester and there was a terrible battle, in which Charles got dreadfully beaten. There was hardly a man left standing, so he couldn't fight any more.

Charles got away from the Battle but he wasn't Safe. For Cromwell had told the Roundheads, "I'll give a lot of money to the man who catches him." So the whole Country was full of Roundheads looking for him.

However, they didn't catch him. For Charles cut off his long hair and dressed in old clothes so as to look like a workman. But he had many adventures before he got safely away. Once when he couldn't find any place to hide in he climbed into an Oak tree and lay there all day. Some of the Roundheads came so close that he could see them and hear them talk.

IT'S LIKE LOOKING FOR a NEEDLE IN A HAYSTACK..

But they never thought of looking up into the tree. So he just stayed quietly there till they had all gone.

At last, after many Narrow Escapes, he got to the seashore, where he found a boat to take him over to France.

Cromwell was now Top Person in the land, but there wasn't any Real Ruler and Parliament was going on in a way Cromwell didn't like.

So one day he marched to Parliament with a whole lot of Soldiers behind him. He left some in the lobby and some on the stairs. Then he went in and sat down and listened to the talking. Suddenly he got up and began to speak. He told the Parliament that they were tyrants and robbers. "For shame," he cried, "go away. Make room for more honest men. I tell you, you are no longer a Parliament."

Then he stamped his foot and the Soldiers rushed in.

As the Soldiers drove out the Members he called Bad Names after them. Then when they'd all been driven out he locked the door and took the key away with him, so that none of them could get in again.

That was the end of the Long Parliament.

"Now," said Cromwell, "I'll have a Parliament that'll do what I want it to." So he sent Messages to a lot of people and told them to come and be a Parliament. And they came.

As this Parliament was made out of Cromwell's Friends they told him, "We think you'd better be King now. We must have some Ruler and you're the Best Person to be it."

"Ah," thought Cromwell, "King Oliver! That sounds Nice." Then he thought a bit more. "No, that wouldn't do. The Army hates Kings. They might hate me if I call myself King Oliver. I can't Risk that."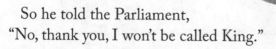

So he told the Parliament, "No, thank you, I won't be called King."

"But we must have a Ruler," they told him, "and he must be Called Something. So what shall it be?"

They thought and thought and at last they said, "How would Lord Protector do?" Everyone said, "That's a Good Idea."

And after that he was called His Highness the Lord Protector.

Very soon, however, Cromwell found that he didn't get on with his New Parliament as well as he had expected. So he just sent them all packing and chose another one. In fact, he made quite a Habit of turning out his Parliaments when they didn't do what he wanted them to. Or sometimes he'd lock the Door of the Parliament House and have the Members sent to him to be lectured like Naughty Schoolboys.

But although Cromwell bullied his Parliaments like anything he did the Ruling well. So the people had Peace and Quiet and got Rested after all the Troubles and Bothers of the Civil War. But they weren't Merry.

There was no more dancing round the Maypole, no more Morris Dancing, no dancing of any kind. There was no more going to Pageants and Plays, no more wearing of Jolly Clothes. All these Things were thought to be Wicked and not what a Sober and God-fearing People should do.

Of course the Cavaliers hated all the Dullness as they hated everything that Cromwell did. So they tried a little Rebelling, but it did no good. For no one could hope to win against a Strong Man like Cromwell with his Ironsides behind him. And for the most part the people were so glad to have some Peace and Quiet that they just put up with it.

But if Cromwell kept Peace at home he did a lot of Fighting abroad.

By this time Holland had got free from the King of Spain. All the people had become Protestants and they had made themselves into a Republic. A Republic means that they didn't have a King.

The Dutch were great Sailors and Adventurers at this time just like the English. So they got quarrelling and tried to spoil each other's trade. They did a lot of fighting at Sea, and Van Tromp, who was a very Famous Dutch Admiral, tied a Broom on to the mast of his ship and said he'd sweep the British ships off the Sea.

But the English too had a great Admiral, who was called Blake. He set out and fought Van Tromp and beat him. So Van Tromp had to take down his Impudent Broom and sweep his own ships home to Holland.

But if Cromwell fought against the Protestant Dutch he was always ready to send an army to help any other Protestants in Europe. And as his Ironsides were such Tremendous Fighters they won lots of Glory.

So, what with winning at Sea and winning on Land, England became as Famous a Top Nation as it had been in the days of Elizabeth.

But the man who had won this Great Fame was a Tyrant. Lots of people hated him, and he knew it. He was so afraid that someone would try to kill him that he always wore armour beneath his clothes. Every night he slept in a different room and never let anyone know in what room he meant to sleep in case they would come to kill him in the night.

Being Busy all day long and never getting a Good Night's Rest he just got Worn Out. Then at last he got too tired to go on living. So he died.

Charles II. The King comes Home

Oliver Cromwell had been far more Autocratic than any Tudor or any Stuart. Like a King he had told the People, "I want my son Richard to do the Ruling after me." And the People had got into such a Habit of Obeying Cromwell that when he died they made Richard Protector.

But it was soon seen that Richard was no good. He couldn't do the Ruling a Bit, and everything got into a jolly fine Mess.

"You're No Good," Parliament told Richard. "You'd better Give Up."

So Richard Gave Up quickly and went home. Then the mess became worse than ever. All sorts of people wanted to be Top Person, so they all began quarrelling. The Cavaliers began Rebelling and the Army went Rampaging Up and Down the Country.

All this time one of Cromwell's Friends called General Monk had been doing the Ruling in Scotland and trying to make the Scots forget about King Charles II. But he knew quite well that he hadn't been able to do it.

Now he left his Ruling in Scotland and came Marching to London. "Hum," he said to himself, when he saw all the Muddle that Things had got into. "Hum, it seems to me that England has had enough of doing without a King."

But instead of talking to anyone Monk wrote to Charles, who was living in Holland. "Will you come back and be our King?" he asked.

"Rather," said Charles. So they wrote some more letters to each other and arranged it all.

Then one day when Parliament was sitting, and all the Members were squabbling like anything, General Monk came in. "There's a Messenger at the Door," he told them. "He's brought a letter from King Charles."

"A Messenger from King Charles. Hurrah! Hurrah!" shouted everyone. "Bring him in, bring him in."

So the Messenger was brought in and the letter read. "I'll pardon everyone (except just a few Very Bad Ones) who went Rebelling against my Father," said Charles in the Letter. "Everyone too will be free to go to the Church he likes Best."

"Splendid!" cried everyone. "That's the kind of King we want. Let's have him back."

And when all the People heard about it they cheered like anything. "God Save the King!" they shouted.

That was the end of the Commonwealth.

A few days after this Charles landed at Dover, and rode merrily up to London through miles of cheering people. The People shouted "God save the King!" and Charles bowed and smiled and waved his hand, joking and laughing with his Friends. "Really," he said, "I don't think I need have stayed away so Long. There doesn't seem to be anyone who isn't pleased to see me."

But the Soldiers weren't pleased. For ten years they had been the Top Persons in the Land. Now here was this Jackanapes with Long Curls like a girl's and a feather in his hat come to lord it over them. Cheer him! Not likely.

Charles saw how the Soldiers hated him, and he said to himself, "I'll be safer with no army than with one that hates me." So he told them, "You can all go home. I don't need you any more." But before they went he paid them all their wages so they couldn't grumble.

While Cromwell had been Ruling in England Charles had been a Poor Homeless Wanderer. But all his troubles hadn't made him Sad and Stern. He liked to laugh and make jokes. He could always see the Funny Side even of his Bothers and Troubles. So he was called the Merry Monarch.

Charles II's first Parliament was called the Cavalier Parliament, for the Members were nearly all Cavaliers instead of being nearly all Puritans as they had been when Cromwell did the Ruling. Being all Cavaliers and the King's Friends you'd have thought that they'd have done everything he wanted them to. But they just didn't. He wanted to let Bygones be Bygones and be Safe. They wanted Revenge.

Charles had really meant to keep his Promises. But he was Lazy and Good-natured in a selfish kind of way, and when he saw how keen his Friends were on having Revenge he just said, "Oh, well, have it your own way." So a lot of the Puritans who had Rebelled against Charles I had their heads chopped off.

The old Bothers about which Church people were to go to began over again too, in spite of what Charles had promised. He didn't care a bit which Church people went to. He really wanted to go to the Roman Catholic Church himself. But he knew the people wouldn't like that so he just went to the English Church. He couldn't see the Sense in quarrelling about it. "Must people always go on hating each other for the Love of God?" he wondered. But when Parliament made Laws which were very hard on everybody who didn't go to the English Church he just let them do it.

Charles II. The Great Plague and the Great Fire of London

In those far-off days people were very dirty and untidy. They used to throw all the rubbish from their houses into the streets and leave it there. Fish heads, mutton bones, cabbage leaves just used to lie and rot and make fearful smells. Nobody seemed to mind the smells, and they never knew that it was very bad for people's Health. People got ill, and died, but they never knew

that it was because the houses and
streets were so dirty.

Some time after Charles II began
to do the Ruling there was a Very
Hot Summer. The hot sun made
the Bad Smells worse than ever.
Soon hundreds and thousands
of people got ill and died. No
one knew how to cure them.
The Doctors were No Good. They never thought of saying,
"Clean your houses, sweep the streets, burn your rubbish."

The King and Parliament went away to Oxford. Everyone who
could went away to the Country or the Sea. So London was left
nearly empty. There were so few people walking about the streets
that grass grew on them. It was all as Quiet as Quiet as could be,
not like a busy, noisy town at all.

All the summer the people went on dying and dying. At last winter came, with frost and snow and cold east winds, and the dreadful sickness ended.

This was called the Great Plague of London. There had been Little Plagues before, but never such a bad one. There has never been another like it again.

At this time nearly all the houses in London were built of wood, and streets were very narrow as well as dirty. The summer after the Great Plague was another hot dry summer, so people hardly needed any fires. But of course a Baker has to have a big fire to bake his bread with. One day when the Baker in Pudding Lane was making bread there was a dreadful smell of burning. He looked about to see what it was and, lo and behold! his shop was on fire.

There weren't any Firemen with Brass Helmets and dashing Red Fire Engines in those days. So the Baker just called, "Fire! Fire!" and all the neighbours came running with buckets of water. But it was No Use. The Fire just blazed and blazed, till the next house too caught fire and the next and next. And as the streets were so narrow the Fire just leapt across to the other side and soon streets and streets were burning.

Everyone came running to help, King Charles and Brother James, Duke of York too. They got their faces and hands all black with the smoke and their fine clothes all dirty and torn. But it didn't matter how hard they worked, the Fire just went blazing on.

For three days and nights the Fire raged on. It was so hot and stifling that people could hardly breathe and what to do no one knew. It seemed as if all London would be burned down.

At last someone said, "I know. Gunpowder. We'll blow up some Streets with gunpowder."

So they got a lot of gunpowder and blew up whole streets of houses so as to make a Big Open Space where there was nothing to burn. That did it. For when the Fire reached the open space it just went out.

That was called the Great Fire of London.

"Oh, what a Dreadful Disaster," said everyone. "Half London burned down. Oh dear, oh dear, what shall we do?"

But it wasn't so bad as it seemed at first. For all the dirty old houses and streets where the Plague had been were burnt up, and with them all that was left of the Plague was burnt up too. When they were built again the houses were better and the streets were wider. But they weren't Very Wide, and if you go to the part of London we call the City you can still see lots of old narrow streets. You can see the Monument too which was built then to remind people about the Great Fire. It has a big bowl of Golden Flames on the top of it.

While the Great Plague and the Great Fire were going on the Dutch and the British were having more Sea Fights. The Dutch got so bold that they actually came sailing up the Thames, sinking English Ships and smashing up houses with their guns.

Oh, what a state the people got into, and oh, how angry they were! To think that any Foreign Foe should dare to sail up Their River! They almost wished the days of Cromwell back again although they had been so Dull. What was the Use of a Merry Laughing King if he let things like that happen? they asked. However, the Dutch were soon beaten off and after a bit the Dutch and the English decided not to quarrel any more. They decided to shake hands and be Friends and join together to Fight the King of France.

At that time the King of France was getting very Uppish and wanted to be the Very Top Person in all Europe. So he started out Conquering. Now the Swedes and Dutch and British all joined together to try to stop him. The English were so pleased at the idea of having a go at their old enemy, the French, that Charles just had to let them join, although he didn't care a bit whether the King of France was Top Person in Europe or not.

But Charles was always wanting money. He spent a tremendous Lot on Revelling and having a Jolly Time. He couldn't always make Parliament give him more when he wanted it, and he never dared to try the old Tricks of getting Money in Wrong Ways, for he didn't want to be sent Packing.

Now he thought of a new way of getting money. He wrote to the King of France and told him, "I won't really fight against you if you'll pay me a lot of money every year. What's more, as soon as I can I'll begin fighting against the Dutch again. That will keep them from Interfering with you."

"All right," said the King of France, "you do that. I'll pay you well."

It was Quite Easy to find an excuse for quarrelling with the Dutch. They were very aggravating. So soon there was another war with them. But the Dutch fought so well that at last Charles got tired of it and made friends with them again. Then he wrote to the King of France and told him, "I'm sorry I can't do any more for you." But he promised not to make Friends with any other country in Europe without asking leave from the King of France. So the King of France still went on paying him money.

Besides all these Fightings abroad Charles had a lot of Bothers at Home. He was always having quarrels with Parliament and telling the Members to go home. People too were always Plotting about something or another. These Plots never came to very much, but they just made people Uncomfortable and Suspicious.

One Worth-While thing to remember is that a Law was made saying that No One was to be put in Prison and left there as long as the King liked. This Law said that everyone who was sent to Prison must be tried before a Judge and either punished or set free. It was called the Habeas Corpus Act. *Habeas Corpus* is Latin for "have the body". It means that the Judges wanted to have the Prisoners brought to be judged.

Charles was rather a Bad Man and he wasn't a Very Good King. But he was Clever and Amusing and had beautiful Manners. So lots of people liked him Very Much and were sorry when he died.

James II of England, VII of Scotland. A Very Stubborn King

Charles II's brother James, Duke of York was Heir to the Throne. He was a Roman Catholic and a Law had been made that no Roman Catholic might be King. But James promised to leave the Protestants alone and as the People didn't want any Fighting and Bothers about who should be King next they just had James.

But some of the Scots didn't want a Roman Catholic King even if he were a Stuart (for the Scots were very fond of the Stuarts). So some of them began Rebelling.

But that didn't do any Good, and their leader the Earl of Argyll had his head cut off.

Almost at the same time James Duke of Monmouth thought that he would try to make himself King. He was James II's nephew and he thought that he had a Better Right to the Throne than James. He had been doing some Plotting while Charles II was on the Throne and Charles had Banished him out of the Country. But a lot of the People liked him very much, so now he came sailing back to England and landed in Dorset, hoping that the country people would join him.

And so they did. "Hurrah! Hurrah!" they shouted. "There's our dear Duke. Come on, let's join him and fight for the Crown." So all the young farmers and miners came running and soon Monmouth had ever such a big army.

But King Monmouth was never crowned and never sat on the Throne. For King James sent an army against him and in the Battle of Sedgemoor Monmouth's men were beaten.

When he was brought before King James he fell on his knees and begged for Mercy. "Won't you forgive me?" he pleaded.

But James never forgave. He didn't even answer his wretched Nephew.

So Monmouth was led away and his head was cut off.

Having put down two Rebellings James felt that he was quite safely seated on the Throne. So he began to think about turning England into a Roman Catholic Country.

He sent a Messenger to the Pope and told him,
"I am your Obedient Servant and I hope that
soon all my people will be too." And
the Pope sent one of his Top Persons
to live in England and help James
with the Ruling. This was against
the Law, for it was Treason to
have anything to do with the
Pope.

The People began to get very
frightened, and angry too. They
couldn't help remembering the
fearful Goings-On of Queen
Mary. The wisest among his Top
Persons warned King James that
the people wouldn't stand his
Goings-On much longer. James
wouldn't listen to them. So they
left him. He just went on doing
things his Own Way.

But the People were quite tired of him and his ways, so they
wrote to the Dutch ruler Prince William of Orange and said,
"Please will you come to be our King? We've had quite enough of
James."

William had some Right to the Throne because he was James
II's Nephew and he had married James II's daughter, who was
called Mary.

"I would like very much to come and be your King," said
William, and he began to get ready.

Then one day someone wrote to James and told him, "Prince
William of Orange is coming to Conquer you. So you'd better
look out."

James turned quite pale as he read the letter, and it dropped out of his hands, they were shaking so. "Oh dear," he said, "I never expected this!"

In a desperate hurry he tried to undo all the Bad Things he'd done. But it was No Use. No one believed in him any more. "He's not sorry," they said, "he's just afraid." So everyone left him and went off to meet the Prince.

William landed at Torbay in Devonshire and came marching to London. All along the way the people crowded to see and cheer him and his Dutch Soldiers. They cheered them because they knew they weren't Foreign Foes come Conquering, but Friends come to free them from a Tyrant.

So with no Bothers at all William and Mary became King and Queen of Great Britain and Ireland, and James ran away to France with his Queen and their baby son James.

This was called the Glorious Revolution.

Mary II and William III.
Bothers in Ireland

As Mary was James II's daughter she had really the Best Right to be Queen, and William ought only to have been Queen's Husband, which is called being Consort. But William was very Haughty. He would have hated like anything not to be as High Up a Top Person as his Wife. He'd rather have gone straight back to Holland than take Second Place. Mary was sweet and gentle and Loving and she didn't want to take the Top Place away from her Husband. So it was arranged that they should both be equal and do the Ruling together. But it really ended in William doing it all mostly.

Most of the English People cheered for joy when William came, but a lot of the Scots and Irish simply hated the idea of having a Dutchman to rule over them. So the Irish wrote to James and said, "Please do come back."

When James ran away from England he went to stay with the King of France, who was called Louis. Louis and William were Deadly Enemies, for Louis was always going Conquering in Holland, and William was always stopping him. So when the Irish People asked James to come back again Louis was delighted. "Here's a Good Chance of annoying William," he said to himself. Then he told James, "You go back to Ireland and I'll help you all I can with Men, Money and Ships."

So with the French King's Men, Money and Ships, James went off to Ireland. Most of the Irish just shouted with Joy when he arrived. But some of them didn't want him. They wanted William to be their King, and they fought like anything.

The French-Irish Army went Rampaging about the Country fighting and going on till William came with a lot more Soldiers. Then in a Battle called the Battle of the Boyne James got badly beaten. After that he gave it up and ran away back to France.

William gets a Bad Mark

When James II first sat on the Throne of England, some of the Scots rebelled and wanted him put off again. Now that he had been put off the Throne a Lot more of the Scots, mostly Highlanders, Rebelled, and wanted him put back again. They went on Rebelling and Rebelling and seemed as if they'd never stop.

At last William said to himself, "This really can't be allowed to go on." So he sent to all the Rebel Chiefs and told them, "If you will promise to stop Rebelling and acknowledge me as your Rightful King I'll forgive you. But if you don't promise before the first of January then you'll be punished."

All the Chiefs promised except one old Chief, MacDonald of Glencoe. He put off making his Promise till the very last day. Then he found that he couldn't make his Promise to just anyone, but that he must go to some High-up Person at Inveraray. He got a Dreadful Fright when he heard that, and started off as quickly as he could.

But the weather was awful and the roads covered with deep snow, so that he could hardly get along. And when at last he arrived he was six days too late. However, the High-up Person took his Promise and said that it would be All Right.

But MacDonald had a Deadly Enemy, Sir John Dalrymple. He was one of William's Top Persons and was called Secretary for Scotland. Dalrymple didn't tell William that MacDonald had given his Promise. He told him instead, "These MacDonalds are just a Gang of Thieves and Robbers. You'd much better kill them all."

Then William signed a paper saying, "Kill them all."

Dalrymple sent a lot of Soldiers to Glencoe. They lived with the MacDonalds for nearly a fortnight as welcome Guests. Early one dark winter morning they rose up and killed all the MacDonalds. Only a few got away in the Darkness and the Snow.

This is called the Massacre of Glencoe. (Massacre means when a whole lot of People are Killed all at once.)

We have to give William a Very Big Black Mark for this. People said he didn't Understand what he was signing. But that's no excuse. It's a King's Business to Understand all about his People and not Sign Things till he's Sure.

As William had Holland to Rule over as well as England he was always going there. While he was away Mary used to do the Ruling in England. She did it so well and was so Sweet and Gentle that the People loved her dearly. And when she got smallpox and died everyone was most dreadfully sorry.

William really thought more about Holland than England. Indeed one of his Chief Reasons for wanting to be King of Great Britain was that he wanted English Ships and Men and Money to help him in his Wars against his Deadly Enemy the King of France. He spent a Dreadful lot of money on these Wars and the British began to get tired of always giving William money for Wars which they weren't really Interested in.

After Mary died William had to be a little more careful. For he knew that the People didn't love him much. It was Mary they had loved. Anything might happen to him if he wasn't careful. Already there had been Plots to kill him.

After a bit, however, Louis and William stopped fighting each other. Louis promised that he'd call William King of Great Britain and Ireland, which he'd never done, and that he wouldn't go helping James.

But before very long William wanted to go fighting Louis again. This time it was because Louis wanted to make his grandson King of Spain, and William didn't want him to. "Well, it's got nothing to do with us," said the English. And very likely they'd have refused to let William go fighting again, only Louis made them angry.

James II died in France. Then Louis went and visited his son and called him James III and Your Majesty and things like that.

"What Impertinence!" said the English. "We'll fight him for that."

So Parliament let William have all the Men, Money and Ships he wanted. But before he could start fighting William died. One day he was out riding and got thrown off his horse who had tripped over a mole hill. It wouldn't have hurt a strong man. But William had never been strong although he had been a Tremendous Fighter.
So he died.

No one was very sorry. People had never liked him much and after Queen Mary died they liked him still less. Although he was King of Great Britain and Ireland for thirteen years he was always just a Dutchman.

Queen Anne. How the Union Jack was Made

The next Queen was Queen Mary's sister Anne. She had a husband called Prince George of Denmark. But he wasn't allowed to be King like William had been. He was just Queen's Husband, which is called being Consort. He was rather stupid and wasn't allowed to do any of the Ruling.

Anne hadn't liked William much or anything he did. But as soon as she was seated on the Throne she said, "Oh yes, I'll go on with that war William was so keen about."

For Anne had a Very Special Clever Soldier called
Marlborough. He wanted a chance to go Conquering and
making himself Famous. Anne was ever so fond of Marlborough
and he could make her do anything he liked. So now she made
him her Top General and sent him off.

All the Top Nations of Europe took a hand in this War which
was got up to stop King Louis of France making his Grandson
King of Spain. It was called the War of the Spanish Succession,
which means a War about which-King-is-to-come-next-in-Spain.
It went on for ten years till all the Top Nations were sick and
tired of it. And in the end Louis had his Own Way and made his
Grandson King of Spain. So it looks rather as if it needn't have
been fought at all. However, we got
Gibraltar out of it.

Meanwhile Marlborough
went Rampaging about all
over Europe winning Big
Battles and making himself
Famous. Anne was frightfully
proud of him. She
made him a Duke, gave him
a whole lot of money and
land, and had a grand Palace built
for him. He called his Palace Blenheim after one
of his Big Battles.

When Marlborough wasn't Rampaging
about Europe winning Big Battles and
lots of Glory he was at home Ruling
Anne. For Anne was very Meek and Mild
and just let herself be ruled by Favourites.
The Duchess of Marlborough ruled Anne
even more than the Duke did. Indeed at

one time the Duke and Duchess seemed to be really King and Queen of England.

But Duchess Sarah had a terrible Temper and used to scold like anything if she didn't get all her Own Way. At last the Queen got tired of her, and afraid of her too. So she sent her away in Disgrace. After a bit Anne got tired of the Duke too. For although he was such a Special Clever Soldier he was dreadfully Greedy. He was always wanting more and more Money. He had a heap of Enemies and they made things very Uncomfortable for him until at last he too was sent away in Disgrace.

The most Worth-While thing to remember of Anne's Reign is that the English and Scottish Parliaments were joined together. Although for a long time now England and Scotland had had the same King there had been two Parliaments, one in Edinburgh and one in London. That wasn't a Very Good Idea, for sometimes the English Parliament went making Laws which were bad for Scotland, and there were no Scottish Members in the English Parliament who could speak out and tell them not to do it.

The wisest people both in England and in Scotland saw that the Best Thing would be to have only One Parliament. But it wasn't easy to make everybody think that. So they talked and talked and shouted at each other and argued like anything. But at length it all got settled.

Besides other Things it was settled that the Country was to be called Great Britain, that there was to be one King, one Parliament and one Flag.

England's Saint was St. George and the Flag of England was a red St. George's Cross on a White ground. Scotland's Flag was a white St. Andrew's Cross on a Blue ground. So to make the Union Flag they put one cross on the top of the other. Then about a hundred years later the Irish joined in too. Their Flag is a Saint Patrick's Cross. It is just the same as St. Andrew's Cross only red and white instead of white and blue. When St. Patrick's Cross was added that made the Union Jack.

And why is our Flag called Jack? Because James I used to be so swanky and sign his name in French – Jacques. It sounds rather like Jack. His Flags came to be called Jacks and when they were all joined together they were called the Union Jack.

ENGLAND
IRELAND
SCOTLAND

Anne wasn't a Great Queen like Elizabeth. She was Good and Kind and got called the Good Queen Anne. But she wasn't very clever at Ruling. She let herself be ruled by her Top Persons. Some of them were Great Men, but often they thought more about having their Own Way about Things than of what was really best for the Country. But still the Country got on very well and was more than ever a Top Nation when Anne died.

George I. The Friends of James do some Rebelling

You remember when James II ran away from William he took his baby son James with him. Baby James was now quite Grown Up. While Anne was doing the Ruling it had been arranged that James was never, never to be made King. The Person who had been chosen to be the next King was a great-grandson of James I. He was called George and was a Sort of King in a Quite Little German Country called Hanover.

This stout old German Gentleman came and sat on the Throne and was called King of Great Britain and Ireland without any Bother at all. That was in England. In Scotland there were still a lot of People who wanted James. Now, they thought, was their Chance. Surely, they said, the People would rather have a handsome young Stuart Prince to rule over them than this fat old German. So they wrote to Prince James and told him, "If you come over to Scotland we're quite sure we can make you King." And James said he'd come.

The Friends of James were called Jacobites, and both in Scotland and in the North of England they began getting

armies ready to fight. But King George sent his Soldiers to stop
them. Then there was a Battle between the King's Men and the
Jacobites, but it was so badly managed that no one knew which
side had won.

"Never mind," said the Jacobites; "we'll beat them well as soon
as King James comes."

At last he came. But oh, what a disappointment he was! Instead
of a gallant young soldier he was a pale-faced, silent man who
never smiled and hardly ever spoke.

He didn't speak and he didn't Do Anything. "Come on, let's
fight," said the Top Persons among the Jacobites. But James
didn't seem to want to fight and when he heard that King
George's soldiers were coming to fight him he sat down and
cried. Then he ran away back to France. Some of the Top Persons
among the Jacobites managed to run away too, others got caught
and had their heads chopped off. And that was the end of that.

Except for this Jacobite Rebelling there was mostly Peace and
Quiet while George I sat on the Throne. He really liked his little
Hanover far better than Great Britain and he was always going
there to see how his German People were getting on. He was
there when he took ill and died.

George II. The Story of Bonnie Prince Charlie

The next King was George I's son. He was called George too.
Like his Father he was Very German, but as by now he'd
lived a good long while in England he could speak some English.
He wasn't very clever but he had a Very Clever Wife called
Queen Caroline, and all the first years of George II's Reign she
really did the Ruling.

It was while George I sat on the Throne that the Top Person in the House of Commons began being called Prime Minister as he is now. George I had a clever Top Minister called Robert Walpole. George II didn't like him much, but Queen Caroline did, and as George nearly always did as Caroline told him he let Walpole go on being Top Minister.

Then after a bit Queen Caroline died and the Jacobites started some more Rebelling.

This time it wasn't James who came but his son Charles. He just thought he'd have a shot at winning the Crown for his Father. So he landed in Scotland one day with only seven Faithful Followers.

The Jacobites weren't too pleased to see him at first. "Go home," said an old Chieftain to him, when he came. "This is no safe place for you."

"I have come Home," said Prince Charles, and smiled at him. And when he smiled people just loved him. They felt they must fight for a Prince who was so handsome and so jolly. They called him "Bonnie Prince Charlie," and gave balls and parties for him, when all the Lovely Ladies were eager to dance with the Bonnie Prince, and all the Brave Men were just as eager to fight for him. So soon Prince Charlie had quite a big Army.

But of course as soon as King George heard of these Goings-On he sent an army to fight Prince Charlie. So one morning there was a Battle at Prestonpans near Edinburgh. Prince Charlie and his Men got up so early that the King's soldiers weren't ready for them. They were only half awake when the Fierce Highlanders came dashing down upon them, and they got such a fright that they just ran away as fast as they could.

After this Grand Victory Prince Charlie said, "Now I must go and Conquer England."

You must remember that in those days there were no trains, and armies just had to walk. So the Prince and his Fierce Highlanders walked and walked day after day till they got to Derby. But instead of being a great Huge Army by the time they got there the army was far smaller than when they set out. For hardly any of the English joined them as Prince Charlie had hoped they would, and a lot of the Highlanders got tired of simply walking and not having any Fierce Fights. So they just went home again.

At Derby all the Top Persons of the Jacobites came to Prince Charlie and told him, "It's no good going any farther. None of these English are going to help us. We'd much better go back to Scotland."

"No, no," said the Prince. "We must go on. I'd rather die than go back now."

He begged and implored, but they wouldn't listen to him, and back to Scotland they trudged the Weary Way.

Had they only known, King George was as frightened as could be, and was all packed up ready to run away. But when he heard that Prince Charlie and his Fierce Highlanders had turned back he decided not to run away. Instead he sent an army after Prince Charlie. So there were some more Battles in Scotland and at the Battle of Culloden Moor Prince Charlie's army was dreadfully beaten.

That was the end. All the Jacobites were scattered, and Prince Charlie had to run away and hide. King George said he'd give a Whole Lot of Money to anyone who could catch him. Heaps of people knew where he was but not one of them told. Not for Worlds would they Betray their Bonnie Prince Charlie. Instead of Betraying him they helped to hide him.

OF COURSE I'd do ANYTHING For him but he does look ABSURD in that dress..

The Most Famous Person who helped him was a Lovely Lady called Flora MacDonald. She dressed Prince Charlie up in girls' clothes and pretended that he was her Maid and so got him safely away from a most Dangerous place where the King's soldiers were looking for him. At last after wandering about for months and months he got to the seashore. There he got into a boat and sailed away to France. He never came back again and the Jacobites never tried any more to put a Stuart King on the Throne.

George II. How Canada was Won

When Henry VII sat on the Throne you remember John Cabot sailed across the Atlantic and found New-found-land, which he claimed for the King of England. After that more and more Daring Sailors crossed the Ocean, always finding out more and more bits of America. Then in the days of Elizabeth men began to try to make a New England across the Seas. But somehow they never managed to do it. Either they got Homesick and came back, or the Red Indians fought them and killed them all, or they got ill and died.

When James I sat on the Throne there were some Puritan kind of people who were very unhappy in England. They didn't like the English Church and wanted to have one just to suit themselves.

So they said, "Let's go to America. We'll still be English there but we'll be free to have our own kind of Church."

So they got a ship called the *Mayflower*, and sailed away on it till they came to America. There they landed and built a town, which they called Plymouth after the town in England from which they'd sailed away. That was the beginning of English people going to live in America, and the people who first went there were called the Pilgrim Fathers.

After that more and more people went to America. By the time of George II there were thirteen different Colonies in America all peopled with Englishmen.

The French too had Colonies in America.

"These British," they said, "are everywhere. If we don't do something to stop them they'll be all over the continent in no time." So they began to build forts so as to keep the British from getting any farther West.

The British Colonists got Very Cross about that for they wanted to be able to spread out as far as they liked. So of course they began quarrelling like anything with the French. These quarrels went on for years and years, always getting worse and worse, until it was plain to see that in All Great Wide America there wasn't room for both the French and the British.

The Top Minister in England at this time was called William Pitt. He was very good at choosing the Best Man when he wanted anything done. So now he sent a young General called James Wolfe out to Canada with a lot of Soldiers.

Wolfe didn't look much like a Great Soldier. He was a pale-faced, red-haired, rather sickly man. But Pitt knew that he was both Brave and Clever.

"You've got to take Quebec, the Capital of Canada," Pitt told him. So off went Wolfe to do it.

But it wasn't so easy. Quebec stands high up on the banks of the great River Saint Lawrence. And although Wolfe and his soldiers sailed up the Saint Lawrence they couldn't find any way of climbing up the steep banks so as to get at Quebec. For the French were very watchful and every path was guarded.

For weeks and weeks Wolfe battered at the Walls of Quebec with his cannon. But it was No Use. It was just like knocking and knocking at a door that wouldn't open. Wolfe knocked and knocked, but the French wouldn't open the door, so he was no nearer getting into Quebec than he had been at the beginning.

Wolfe got dreadfully worried with it all. He got so worried that he fell ill. But he wouldn't Give Up. At last one day when he was scouting round he found a steep little path which led up the cliff.

It was so steep and so narrow that the French thought no one but a cat could climb up it. So they didn't bother to guard it very well.

"Where a cat can go a Highlander can go," said Wolfe to himself, for he had some Highlanders with him. "And that's the way we'll all go."

So one dark night Wolfe and his men were rowed

across the River to the foot of the little Path. Quietly, quietly they went so as not to let the French hear them. Then quietly, quietly the climb began. Up and up went the soldiers panting and struggling. Oh, but it was a stiff climb. But at last they were up. And when the sun rose there was the British Army standing on the plain outside Quebec.

The French fought very bravely but they got beaten. Quebec was taken and Canada became a British Possession.

George III. How the English Colonies became the United States of America

Very soon after the taking of Quebec, George II died. No one was very sorry, for the People couldn't *love* a fat old German who thought more about his petty little Hanover than about Great Britain and all its Colonies.

The next King was George II's Grandson. He was called George too, but he had been born in England and could speak English quite well. He was young and not bad-looking, so the People said, "There now, it looks as if we are getting back to having a proper English King again." So everybody was pleased.

Ever since the days of Queen Elizabeth Daring Sailors had gone sailing the seas and finding out new Lands. Now a Bold Captain called Captain Cook was always sailing into unknown seas, and when he found any new Land he just claimed it for King George.

One day when he was sailing about he found the North Island of New Zealand. So he landed, cut the name of his Ship on a tree and planted a pole with a Union Jack on it. "There now," he said, "there is a New Island for King George." The next year he went out looking for more land and found the South Island of New Zealand, so he claimed that too for King George. And to make quite sure that he wasn't missing anything he just claimed any other Islands that might be anywhere near too.

"There seem to be lots of Islands in the Pacific Ocean," said Captain Cook to himself, "I'd better go again and see if I can find anything else." So off he went, and this time he found Australia.

Australia is the very biggest Island in the whole Wide World. Of course when Captain Cook found it he set up the Union Jack and claimed it for King George. So a lot more was added to the British Empire. But very soon King George lost another big bit of it.

When Quebec was taken and Canada became British the Colonists in America were very joyful. "Now that we have got rid of those bothersome French," they said, "we can have some Peace and Quiet. We can go where we like and do what we like without having to fight them."

But it just didn't happen like that.

As you know War always costs a lot. It has got to be paid for somehow and it generally means More Taxes.

Soon the Top Persons in Parliament said, "Look here, we fought this War in Canada to make the American Colonists more Comfortable. They wanted to get rid of the French and we got rid of the French for them. So the American Colonists ought to pay for the War. Let's tax them."

"Yes," said King George; "that's a Good Idea. It's only fair that they should pay for their Own War."

When King George told the American Colonists, "I'm going to make you pay taxes to pay for the War we had getting rid of the French for you," the colonists said, "Oh no, you can't do that. You don't let us choose any Members to go to Parliament. If we are to pay taxes we must have a share in making the Laws, and send Members to Parliament like England and Scotland do."

"Nonsense," said King George. "I say you are to pay taxes, so there's an end of it."

"Well, we just won't pay them," said the Colonists. And they made so much Bother about it that at last King George and his Top Persons said, "All right, we'll let you off all the taxes except one. You must pay a tax on Tea."

King George kept on this one tax just to show the Colonists that he wasn't Beaten and that he could make them pay taxes if he liked.

But to the Colonists it seemed that if they paid one tax they might just as well pay them all. It wasn't so much the Money that they minded about (although they minded that too), as the Idea that it wasn't Fair.

They made up their minds that they wouldn't pay even one tax.

However, King George and his Top Ministers didn't pay any Attention to them and some ships full of Tea were sent to America.

When these Ships arrived in Boston Harbour there was a great Fuss. All the Top Persons got together and talked. "What are we to do?" they asked. "That Tea mustn't be landed. If it is we're done for. Once that Tea gets ashore there'll be no keeping our womenfolk from buying it."

But while they were talking and trying to think what to do, a Whole Lot of daring young Americans dressed themselves up like Red Indians. With wild War-Whoops they ran to the harbour and dashed aboard the Tea-ships. They seized the Tea-chests, smashed them open with their Hatchets, and poured the Tea into the sea. Chest after chest, chest after chest, was burst open and the Tea poured out until the sea was black with Tea.

"Oh dear," said the Married Ladies, "what Waste! Think of all the pots of Tea we might have had."

But no one tried to stop the Make-Believe Red Indians. It was the greatest Tea-Making that ever was seen, and for long after it was called the "Boston Tea-Party".

When King George heard about this Tea-Party he was Very Angry, and he began to do all sorts of things to Punish the Americans for their Bad Behaviour. But the Americans weren't a bit Sorry for what they had done, and the way King George treated them simply made them furious. "If he isn't careful," they said, "we'll fight him."

"Nonsense," said King George. "They'll only behave like Lions as long as we behave like Lambs. When they see that I mean to be Firm, they'll soon be Meek enough."

But the Americans weren't Meek at all and so at last it came to War.

The Colonies had never been very friendly with each other. Indeed sometimes they had been very quarrelsome. But now they all joined together to fight the British. Their Top Person was called George Washington. He was Brave and a Clever Soldier and had done a lot of fighting already against the French. So he was very good at it.

At first the Colonists hadn't really meant to leave off being part of the British Empire. But before they'd been fighting for very long they decided that they wouldn't belong to it any more.

So they had a great Meeting and wrote out a long Paper. In this Paper they said that they were going to be a Free Country all on their own and have nothing more to do with Great Britain. Their Country was to be called the United States of America and it was to be a Republic, which means that they would have no King. This was called the Declaration of Independence.

Great Britain had chased the French out of America so as to make the Colonists more comfortable. Now these same French came back and helped the Americans to fight the British. That was a very Bitter Blow to the British. Some of them wanted to stop fighting at once and let the Americans have their Own Way. King George said, "No." So the War went on. But it was No Use. So at last King George gave it up and let the Americans go free. In this way Great Britain lost all her American Colonies. If King George hadn't been so Obstinate and his Top Persons so Stupid it might never have happened.

George III. "England Expects That Every Man Will Do His Duty"

S ome time after the French had been helping the Americans they began to have a dreadful lot of Bothers at home. They had a kind of Civil War, when they cut off the heads of their King and Queen and said they would have no more Kings. There were to be no more Lords either and everyone was to be Equal.

That went on for some time, then a Clever young Soldier called Napoleon Bonaparte upset it all again.

When Napoleon began he was Quite Poor, but he was so clever that he rose and rose till he made himself Top Person in the French Army. After that he went on making himself more and more Famous until he got to be Top Person in all France. Then he had himself Coronated and called the Emperor of the French.

But being Top Person in France wasn't enough for Napoleon. He wanted to be Top Person in Europe. So he went out Conquering. He conquered a whole lot of Kings. Then he took their Thrones and Crowns and gave them to his Brothers and Friends.

Napoleon was Dreadfully Anxious to Conquer Great Britain too. So he gathered a Great Big Army together and called it the Army of England. By that he meant the army that was going to conquer England. He gathered a lot of ships too, and he made so sure of winning that he got a Medal ready to celebrate his Victory. On it he put "Made in London", which of course wasn't true.

Napoleon said to himself, "I'd better begin with Ireland. It won't be difficult to Conquer the Irish, for a lot of them don't like the English and they'll be quite ready to help me."

Up to this time the Irish still had a Parliament of their own. Now the Top Persons in England began to think that it would be Much Better to have only One Parliament for the Whole Country. "If the Irish sent Members to the British Parliament," they said, "they could do their Grumbling at Westminster, and perhaps there wouldn't be so many Bothers in Ireland."

"Yes," said others, "that's a Good Idea, and it would make it more difficult for Napoleon to go Conquering in Ireland."

At first the Irish didn't like the Idea much. But after a lot of talking it got settled. The Irish Parliament was given up, and English, Scottish, and Irish Members all joined together at Westminster. Then Saint Patrick's Cross was added to the Flag and the Union Jack was made like we have it now.

At the same time King George had another Good Idea. "What's the Use," he said, "of going on calling myself King of France? I'm not King of France, so I won't be called that any more. I'll be called George III by the Grace of God, of the

United Kingdom of Great Britain and Ireland, King, Defender of the Faith."

While these things were going on at Home, the War was still going on Abroad. However, everyone got tired of fighting, so at length they made Peace.

But Peace did not last long and the next year Napoleon got ready to Conquer Britain. The British too got ready to give him the kind of Welcome he wouldn't like. Day and night a watch was kept along the shores so that the People could be warned as soon as the French boats came in sight.

They never came. For while the soldiers were watching for them on land the sailors were watching for them on sea. The Top Person in the Navy was the Great Admiral Lord Nelson. He was very Brave and Daring and had done lots of Sea Fights. He had been wounded a lot too and had lost one eye and one arm, but in spite of that he just went on being brave and daring.

The Spaniards had joined with the French, and Nelson knew that there were a whole lot of Spanish and French ships somewhere. So he went looking for them, and at last he found them all together in Trafalgar Bay, which is off the Coast of Spain.

Nelson knew that there was going to be a Very Big Fight. Every Captain in the whole Fleet had been told what to do, but Nelson felt that something was wanting. So from his own Ship, the Victory, a Message was spelled out in little flags so that the whole Fleet could read it. The Message was, "ENGLAND EXPECTS THAT EVERY MAN WILL DO HIS DUTY," and when the Sailors saw it they cheered like anything.

Every man did do his duty and the Battle of Trafalgar was a Very Great Victory for the British. But sad to say the Great Admiral got killed. His last words were, "Thank God, I have done my Duty."

After Trafalgar Napoleon had to give up the Idea of
Conquering Britain, so he thought he'd try something else, and
he made up his mind to spoil British Trade. "You're not to buy
anything from the British," he told all the countries in Europe.
And as most of the countries in Europe were afraid of Napoleon
they pretended to obey him. But really it wasn't much Use, for
Britain was the great Manufacturing Country of Europe and all
the other countries needed the things that Britain had to sell.

Portugal was one of the countries that still went on buying
things from the British. That made Napoleon Very Angry and he
went off Conquering in Portugal. After that, he took the King
of Spain prisoner and gave the Throne of Spain to his brother
Joseph Bonaparte.

But the Spanish people began Rebelling and asked the British to help them.

This was called the Peninsular War because it was fought in the Peninsular which is made by Spain and Portugal. The Top Person on the British side was a great General called Arthur Wellesley. Later on, because he was such a clever soldier, he was made the Duke of Wellington. The War went on for years, but at last the French were chased right out of Spain and the Spaniards got their own King back again.

While the Peninsular War was going on Napoleon left the fighting there to his Top Generals and went off Conquering in Russia. But he couldn't conquer Russia. Instead he lost nearly all the great Army he'd taken with him. And when he got back to France the people were so angry with him that they put him off the Throne and Banished him to a little Island in the Mediterranean called Elba.

Then all the People that Napoleon had conquered began rejoicing. But all over Europe things were in a pretty Fine Mess. So a lot of the Top Persons got together and began talking and talking and trying to arrange things again.

But while they were talking Napoleon grew tired of living quietly in Elba. So one day he just got into a boat and came sailing over to France. He was a cruel, Selfish man, but he was the Soldiers' Favourite, and when they saw him again they came running to join him. So quite soon he had a Big Army.

When they heard about these Goings-On the Top Persons who were gathered together talking and talking got a terrible Fright. They hadn't been able to agree about what it was best to do to tidy up the Mess Napoleon had made in Europe. But now they all agreed at once, "We've got to join together and fight him," they said. "We can't allow him to come back and go Rampaging about Europe like he used to do."

Napoleon went marching out to meet them and a Big Battle was fought at Waterloo, near Brussels. The Top Person on the British side was of course the Duke of Wellington. Napoleon was quite pleased to have the chance of beating Wellington. But it just didn't happen like that. It was Napoleon who got beaten.

He got beaten so badly that he saw there was no Hope of ever getting back to the Throne of France. So he went to the British and told them, "You've always been a Very Noble Enemy. I hope you'll be kind to me."

But it wasn't easy to be kind to a Dangerous Man like Napoleon. All the Kings and Peoples of Europe were afraid of him. So it was decided to Banish him to a lonely Island in the Atlantic Ocean called Saint Helena. There he stayed till he died.

George III went on being King for years and years until he became a Very Old Man. He wasn't a very wise King and sometimes he was quite mad. All the last part of his Reign he was mad and blind too, so he couldn't do the Ruling. The Prince of Wales did it and was called the Regent. A Regent means a Person who does the Ruling for a King.

Although there was such a terrible lot of Fighting while George III sat on the Throne, none of it was in England. So the People just went on quietly making things and selling them to all the people in Europe who were far too busy fighting to find time to make things for themselves. So the country got richer and richer. By this time too people had learned how to make machinery and how to use steam to make the machinery go, and England became the Workshop of Europe.

George IV. The First Gentleman in Europe

When George III died the Prince of Wales became King and was called George IV. As George III had sat on the Throne for such a long time, George IV was rather old when he began being King. He wasn't really a very Nice Man, but he was rather good-looking and had beautiful manners. He dressed very grandly too, so he got called the First Gentleman in Europe.

You remember that after the Gunpowder Plot people had got very afraid of the Roman Catholics and a lot of Laws had been made which were very hard on them. They weren't allowed to be Members of Parliament or be Officers in the Army or Navy or serve their Country in any way.

For a long time Wise People had seen that these Laws were very Unfair and had tried to do away with them. They had tried when George III was sitting on the Throne. But George III was an obstinate old man and he wouldn't hear of it. Now they tried again.

A lot of the Irish were Roman Catholics and as George IV had said he loved them so much during a Visit there, Top Persons in Parliament felt sure that he'd be quite willing to do away with these old Laws.

But George IV wouldn't hear of it either. "My Father would have had his head chopped off rather than do away with these laws," he said. "I'd have my head chopped off too rather than give way."

But the days when Kings could be Tyrants were gone. So in spite of his grand words George was forced to give way. The old Laws were done away with and after that Roman Catholics could be anything they liked just the same as everybody else.

A Most Exciting Thing happened about now. That was the First Train. Up to now when anyone wanted to go on a journey they had to drive. If you had lots of money you went in your own carriage with four horses and sometimes with six. The roads were Dreadful. In winter they were thick with mud and in summer just as thick with dust. So it took at least four horses to drag the carriage along.

If you hadn't a carriage you went in a Stage Coach. That was a kind of bus with four or six horses. Some people went inside and some outside. Travelling was very slow and uncomfortable and lots of people never travelled at all.

People had found out how to make steam work machines in factories. Now some Clever Men said why shouldn't we make steam drag things along?

So they began making Experiments, and at last they made a little Puffing Billy of an Engine with a tall chimney that could drag a little train along rails. "Oh, how interesting," said everyone, "but of course they'll never be Much Use because they can only go along rails. We can't possibly have Special roads with rails on them all over the place. They would be so Ugly and the Country would all get spoilt with the smoke."

A whole lot of people tried their Very Best to stop Railroads being made, but a whole lot more people did their Very Best to have them made. They won. And in time there were Railroads nearly all over the Country.

Sir Robert Peel was Top Minister at this time and he had some very Good Ideas. One was Policemen. There hadn't been any proper Policemen, so now Robert Peel said, "We really must have proper ones. They must be Tall, Strong men so that they can take bad people off to Prison easily. They must be Nice, Kind men so that they can take care of Little Children when they're lost and help Old Ladies and Little Children too to cross the road and all that sort of thing."

So he got some tall, kind men and dressed them in blue clothes and called them Policemen. But a lot of people called them Peelers, because it was Robert Peel who first thought of them. Other people called them Bobbies, and Bobbies is still our Pet name for our Nice Policemen.

Although George IV had such fine manners the people didn't love him. So when he died no one was very sorry.

William IV. The Slaves are Made Free

The next King was George IV's brother. He was called William IV, and he was quite an old gentleman when he began being King.

William IV had been in the Navy, so he got called the Sailor King. He liked to live a simple life and used to go walking about London all by himself, just like anybody else. He didn't bother much about the Good-of-the-People or doing the Ruling well.

One Worth-While thing to remember is that the people in the British Empire gave up having Slaves.

For a long time people had been in the Habit of stealing People from their homes in Africa and selling them to people who wanted work done. These poor people were taken to Market and sold just as if they were sheep or cows. Most of them were bought by the Colonists in the West Indies. Those Colonists used to grow a lot of Sugar Cane to make Sugar out of and they needed a lot of people to do the work. They didn't pay the people any wages and sometimes the Masters were very unkind to their slaves.

In Far-off Days people never thought about whether their slaves were happy or not. But as time went on some Good Men tried to make others see how wicked it was to buy men and women just as if they were sheep or cows and make them work hard without paying them any wages.

One of these good men was called Wilberforce. For a long time he worked hard trying to make people see how wicked Slavery was. At last he made a lot more people think as he did and they made up their minds that all Slaves must be made Free.

But the Planters in the West Indies said, "Oh no, you can't do that. We should be ruined. We must have Slaves to do the work in our fields. Besides, think of all the money we've spent in buying our Slaves. Are we to lose all that?"

"Oh no," said Parliament, "we'll pay back all the money you've spent on buying slaves. So you must let them go Free and not buy any more."

At last it was settled and all the Slaves were set Free. After that they still went on working, but the Planters had to pay them wages instead of making them work for nothing.

William IV had been rather old when he began being King so he didn't reign very long. He was good-natured but rather stupid, so the People didn't respect him very much, and they didn't feel very sad when he died.

Victoria. A Girl Queen

Oh dear," said a little girl called Victoria to herself, "oh dear, I do have a lot of lessons to learn! I'm sure I've far more lessons than other little girls. It isn't Fair."

Now one day Victoria found a page in her History Book which showed how Kings and Queens came after each other. It showed who was the Heir-to-the-Throne.

"Oh, this is very Interesting," said Victoria, and she read the page very carefully. Then she looked at her governess. "I see now," she said, "why I have such a lot of lessons to learn. I shall be Queen when Uncle King dies. Oh, I will be good, I will be good."

The Person whom Victoria called Uncle King was William IV. Her Dear Papa had died when she was a baby (or he would have been the next King), and Victoria lived with her Dear Mama in Kensington Palace.

Victoria and her Dear Mama were rather poor for such High-up People, and Victoria didn't have many Grand Parties or much Fun. She just went on quietly learning the things a Queen must know if she is to be a Good Queen, and keeping her clothes tidy and working in her own little garden until she was a nearly Grownup Young Lady of eighteen.

how CAN I be QUEEN? I've only got This HAT for a CROWN

Then one night a carriage dashed out of the gates of Windsor Castle and went tearing along the road to London as fast as it could go. In the carriage was the Archbishop of Canterbury and another High-up Person called the Lord Chamberlain.

It was five o'clock in the morning when the carriage got to Kensington Palace, and the two Top Persons got out and began knocking at the door. At last a sleepy servant opened the door.

"We have come to see Princess Victoria," said the Top Persons.

"Oh, you can't do that," they were told. "She's in bed asleep."

"Well she must get up," said the Archbishop. "We've come to see The Queen."

The Queen! That was quite a different story.

So Victoria was wakened. As soon as they saw her the two grand Top Persons knelt down on the floor and kissed her hand. "His Majesty King William is dead," they told her, "and now you're Queen."

Then after some more talk they said goodbye, and Victoria went upstairs again.

"I'm sorry about poor Uncle King," she said to herself. "But how splendid to be a Queen!"

Soon after she began to do the Ruling, Victoria married her German Cousin Prince Albert. But although Albert was married to a Queen he wasn't allowed to be called King. Victoria loved him ever so much, but she couldn't bear to think of anyone being as High Up a person as she was. "Oh no," she said, "I must be Queen all by myself. I can't have anyone else mixing themselves up with the Ruling." So Albert was just a Queen's Husband who is called Consort. However, he was Very Clever and Very Good. So Victoria got to love him more and more, and in the end she got rather sorry that she couldn't let him be King.

By this time there were far more people in Great Britain than there used to be and the Farmers didn't grow enough wheat to make bread for them all. So bread went on getting dearer and dearer till at last poor people couldn't make enough money to buy it with.

There was plenty of wheat in other countries, but it couldn't be brought to England because some time before this Parliament had made a Law saying that no wheat was to be brought to England until English wheat was Very, Very Dear. Parliament made this Law meaning to be kind to the Farmers so that they could make a lot of money. But at last a lot of the Top Persons saw how dreadful it was for the Poor People always to be Hungry. So they began fighting like anything to get the Corn Laws, as they were called, done away with.

You'd have thought that it would have been quite easy to make Everybody see how dreadful it was. But lots of the Top Persons just wouldn't see it. So the Top Persons who wished to do away with the Corn Laws had to go on Talking and Writing about it for ever so long.

And while they were Talking and Writing things got still worse. Nearly all the Poor People in Ireland lived on Potatoes, and the Potatoes all went Bad. In a few weeks the food that should have lasted a Whole Year went rotten.

This was such a Dreadful Misfortune that it made Everyone see how Bad the Corn Laws were and they hurried up and did away with them as fast as ever they could. But they weren't fast enough and lots of the poor people in Ireland died.

When people heard how the poor Irish had nothing to eat everybody sent food and money to help them. The Captains of the Ships said, "We won't charge anything for carrying food to Ireland." The Railway people said, "All parcels for Ireland go free. Just put "For Ireland" on the parcel and you needn't pay anything." So at last everybody had enough to eat and the Corn Laws were done away with.

Victoria. Peace and War

Although the Prince Consort wasn't allowed to be called King he helped Victoria with the Ruling a Whole Lot. He thought about the Good-of-the-People and took an Interest in the Trade-of-the-Country too.

The next thing to settle was where the Exhibition was to Be. There wasn't any place big enough in London to hold a Great Exhibition. So something would have to be built. It would have to be built quickly too.

The British hadn't been doing any Fighting for years and years. You would think with a plump little Lady sitting on the Throne and with her clever Husband helping her there wouldn't be any fighting. But there just was.

The Russians and the Turks began quarrelling with each other and the Russians wanted to chase the Turks out of Europe. For some reason the French didn't want them to do that and neither did the British. So these two old enemies, the French and the British, shook hands and made friends and went off together to help the Turks.

All the Fighting was in the Black Sea and in the bit of Russia called the Crimea. So it was called the Crimean War. In Winter it is dreadfully cold in Russia; far, far colder than in England and Scotland. The poor soldiers got ill with the cold. A lot of them got wounded too and there were no proper Hospitals and no proper Nurses, so the soldiers were very, very unhappy.

Then a lady called Florence Nightingale heard about it, and she said, "I must go to Russia and help to nurse our poor soldiers and make them well again."

No one had ever thought of having Lady Nurses for the Soldiers and a lot of the officers didn't want to have them now. "A war is no place for women," they said. "We can do quite well without them."

However, Florence Nightingale was allowed to go and to take some more nurses with her. When they got to Russia they found everything in a dreadful Mess. The Hospitals were dirty. The poor soldiers had no clean sheets or soft pillows and beds, or any of the things that make sick people comfortable and help to make them well again.

But Florence and her Nurses worked hard and soon the Hospitals were sweet and clean and the men began to get well. The Soldiers just loved her and she never seemed to get tired of doing things for them. Long after everyone else had gone to

bed she would walk through the wards carrying a Lamp in her hand. She would pass quietly from bed to bed doing anything she could to comfort the sick and wounded men and make them go to sleep. So she got called The Lady with the Lamp.

Since Florence Nightingale worked among the Soldiers in the Crimea there have always been Army Nurses. When the Knights of old went to do a war of the Cross they wore Red Crosses on their armour. Now Army Nurses wear Red Crosses too.

The Crimean War went on for nearly two years. In the end Russia was beaten and the Turks weren't chased out of Europe.

Not long after this the British had to go fighting again. This time it was in India.

Ever since the days of the Tudors the British had been getting more and more Important in India. Everything seemed to be going on nicely when all of a sudden the Indian Soldiers, who were called Sepoys, began rebelling. This was called the Indian Mutiny.

It all began really because of a mistake. The Sepoys weren't Christians but Mohammedans and Brahmins and people like that. Their Religions forbade them to touch certain kinds of Fat and the Sepoys got it into their heads that the British were going to make them touch these Fats. It wasn't true. But the Sepoys Rebelled.

It was a dreadful time for all the British people who were in India. At one time it seemed almost as if they would be chased right out of the country. But Britons are Very Brave and Very Dogged. So in the end they won. The Mutiny came to an end and the country became peaceful again.

Up to this time Victoria hadn't really done the Ruling in India. But now the Top Persons decided that she ought to do it. But of course the Queen had to live in England and do the Ruling there. So she sent a Very Top Person out to India to do the Ruling for her. This Top Person was called a Viceroy, which means someone who does the Ruling for a King or Queen.

Some years after this Edward Prince of Wales went to pay a Visit to India. At first when the Indian Princes heard that he was coming they weren't very pleased about it. But Prince Edward had such a way with him that he made everybody like him. Soon the Indian Princes were all trying to see who could give him the most splendid Welcome. They had lots of grand Parties for him and loaded him with presents. And after he came Home Victoria got called Empress of India.

Victoria. The Empire grows Bigger and Bigger

Some time before this Victoria's Dear Husband Albert had died. She was so sad about it that she felt sure she would soon die too. But she didn't. Indeed she went on doing the Ruling for years and years, always getting more and more people to rule over.

For a long time after Captain Cook found the Islands of New Zealand hardly any people went to live there because they were frightened. The people who lived in New Zealand were called Maoris. They were Brave and told the Truth and Kept their Word. But they had one Dreadful Fault. They were fond of eating people. So of course no one wanted to go and make their homes in a place where they ran the Risk of being eaten up.

However, a Missionary heard of these people. He wasn't a bit afraid of them and he went to New Zealand and taught them to be good, and quite quickly they gave up their horrid habit.

Then a lot of people went and made their homes in New Zealand. But they hadn't any Parliament or Governor or anyone to do the Ruling properly. So Victoria sent a Governor to New Zealand. He settled things up with the Great Maori Chiefs and made friends with them. And so New Zealand became an Important Part of the British Empire and had its own Parliament and own Top Minister.

A lot of people had begun going to Australia too. They were Farmers mostly and they grew lots of corn and had great flocks of Sheep. Then after a bit Gold was found and still more people went to dig up the gold and make lots of money.

More and More people kept going to Australia until it became an Important Part of the British Empire with its own Parliament and its own Top Minister.

Time went on and the Queen grew old. For fifty years she had sat upon the Throne. For fifty years she had done the Ruling.

Then there were great Rejoicings, which were called The
Jubilee. The streets were decorated with Flags and Streamers
as the Queen drove to Westminster Abbey to give Thanks to
God. Kings and Princes from all over the World rode before her.
Behind them, all alone, in a great carriage came a little Old Lady
dressed in black. It was the Queen. And as she passed the people
cheered and shouted till they were hoarse.

Ten years went past. Victoria still sat on the Throne; she still
did the Ruling. But she was getting very tired. She was getting
very old.

Once again there were great rejoicings. Princes from India and
the Top Persons from all the Great Dominions and Colonies,
were asked to come; from all the scattered Islands of the Sea,
from every far-away place that belonged to the Empire they
were asked. So surrounded only by her own Subjects the little
Old Lady drove through the gay streets once more with the
bells ringing and guns thundering and the People Cheering and
Cheering and Cheering. For they loved the little Old Lady who
was the Queen.

This was called the Diamond Jubilee.

The British hadn't had to do any War for quite a long time. But
soon after these peaceful Doings they had to fight once more.

Long ago when Cromwell was doing the Ruling some Dutch
people sailed away and made their homes in South Africa. After
they had been there for some time they weren't called Dutch any
more. They got called Boers, which really means Farmers. Later
on some British people went there too to find new Homes. As
you remember the British and the Dutch used to quarrel a lot
at Home. When they went to South Africa they still went on
quarrelling. In the part of South Africa called the Transvaal the
Top People who did the Ruling were Boers, although there were
far more British than Boers there. The British had to pay taxes,

but they weren't allowed to do any of the Ruling. They weren't allowed to choose Members of Parliament or to help in any way to make the laws. So they began grumbling like anything.

But grumbling didn't do a bit of good. The Boers just said, "Well, if you don't like the way we treat you, you can go away. We don't really want you here – we'd rather you went away and left us to ourselves."

But the British didn't want to go. Things just got worse and worse until at last it came to fighting.

It was a horrid war and many people felt very sad about it. Perhaps if the British had been a little more patient it needn't have been fought. Anyhow it was fought and the Boers got beaten. So the whole of South Africa became part of the British Empire. A very Important part it was too.

But Victoria never knew about that. For she was very tired and very old, and one day while the war was still going on the News was sent through all the Empire that the Queen was very ill. A few days later came the still sadder News, "The Queen is dead." Then all over the Wide World wherever the Union Jack was flown the People mourned. Never in the long story of our Island had a Queen been so loved. Never had the Empire been so full of grief, for everyone felt that they had lost a Friend.

Edward VII. The King who Loved Peace

The Prince of Wales now became King. He was called Edward VII, and the Lovely Lady who was his wife was called Queen Alexandra.

Although Edward had lived among his People for so long they didn't know him much. For Victoria had liked to do all the Ruling herself.

Now said the People, "What sort of King is he going to be?" They needn't have bothered, for King Edward soon showed them that he was going to be a Very Good King and a Very Clever one too.

King Edward thought a lot about the Good-of-the-People. He knew that the Best Thing for a country was to be at Peace and not have any Fighting to do. He knew too that just at this time, for one reason or another, a whole lot of the other Peoples in Europe didn't like the British much and didn't want to be Friends with them.

"I must try to make them be Friends with us," said Edward. So he went and paid visits to all the Top Persons in Europe. He was so nice to them and he made them all like him so much that after he had been to see them they all wanted to be friends with the British.

One of the Top Persons Edward went to visit was the Emperor of Austria. It was the first time that a King of England had visited Austria since the days of Richard the Lion-Heart. Then you remember the Emperor put Richard in Prison. But these Bad old Days were long past. This time the King of England was an Honoured Guest and had a very nice visit.

There was only one of the Top Persons that Edward didn't get on with. That was his Nephew William, Emperor of Germany. The fact was William wanted to be the Very Most Top Person in all Europe, and he didn't like his Uncle going about making everyone like him and be Friends with him. He thought that Uncle Edward was trying to make himself the Very Most Top Person and he was jealous. He never seemed to think that he too could go about and make Friends with everyone just the same as Uncle Edward did.

King Edward did the Ruling very well and kept the Peace he loved. For nine years he sat on the Throne and the more the People got to know him the better they loved him, and they hoped that he would go on doing the Ruling for a long, long time.

But Edward was getting to be quite an Old Gentleman and his Bronchitis was very bad. It got so bad at last that he died.

Oh, how sad the People were! They were sadder even than when Victoria died. And when they thought of poor lovely Queen Alexandra left all alone they felt more sorry still.

George V. A Very Much-loved King

The Prince of Wales now became King. He was called George V and the stately Lady who was his Wife was called Queen Mary.

There was Peace and Quiet when George V first sat on the Throne. But before very long the Peace and Quiet was all smashed to Bits.

WHAT A LOVELY MORNING

WHAT SHALL I DO AFTER LUNCH?...

One day a wicked man killed the Heir-to-the-Throne of Austria. The man was a Serbian and because of his wicked deed the Emperor of Austria wanted to punish the whole of the Serbians. He wanted to punish them so much that they would no longer be a Free People.

When the Top Person in Russia, who was called the Czar, heard that he was angry. "I won't allow you to do that," he said, and he began to get ready to fight.

"Oh, very well," said the Top Person in Germany, who was called the Emperor, "if you are going to fight against Austria we'll fight against you. And we'll fight against your Friends the French too."

The Emperor William didn't really mind about the Heir-to-the-Throne of Austria being killed. But he was very Uppish and wanted to make himself the Very Top Person in all Europe. So he said to himself, "This is a Grand Chance for me to go Conquering. I've got a far better Army than these other Peoples and I'll easily beat them and make myself Top Person in Europe."

One after another all the Top Nations in Europe took sides, some for Serbia and some against, and began to get ready to fight.

Of course all this had nothing to do with Britain. King George loved Peace and Quiet and he didn't want to quarrel with anyone. But the British too were forced to join in.

Belgium is a little country and in the days Long Ago when the Top Nations were quarrelling they used to go trampling through Belgium and fighting battles there. But a good many years before this all the Top Nations had agreed that this wasn't Fair. So they had promised that however much they were quarrelling with each other they would leave Belgium alone. They promised that no Army should ever march through Belgium.

But the Germans and the French had been Bitter Enemies for ever so long. The German Emperor wanted terribly to beat the French and the quickest way to get to France was through Belgium. So he just said, "Come on, there's no one to stop us. We'll just march through Belgium."

"Oh no," said King George when he heard about it, "we can't allow that. We promised the Belgians that we wouldn't allow it and we must keep our Promise."

So George told his Cousin Emperor William, "You've broken your Promise so we'll have to fight you for that."

Once again Great Britain was at war and not only Great Britain but the whole British Empire. From every part of the Empire soldiers came to help Great Britain. They came from Canada, India, Australia, New Zealand, South Africa, and from every country all over the Wide World where the Union Jack was flown.

It was a perfectly horrid War – the worst that had ever been fought – and so many Nations joined in that it was called the World War. The chief Nations on the Wrong Side were Germany and Austria. The chief Nations on the Right Side were at first France and Great Britain. Later on the United States of America joined them.

So many of the British went away to fight that there weren't enough men left at Home to do the work of the Country. So the Women said, "We'll do it."

Then women began to do work on the Farms. They did Sowing and Ploughing and Reaping. They made hay and looked after the Cows, and did all kinds of work that has to be done on Farms.

Women became Milkmen, Postmen, Bus Conductors, and Railway Porters. In fact, they did nearly every kind of Man's work that you can think of. A lot of them went to the War too and became Nurses like Florence Nightingale. Others stayed at Home and nursed the poor Sick Soldiers when they came back from the War.

For more than four years this
dreadful War went on. Then
at last it came to an end. The
British and their Friends
won and the Germans and
their Friends were beaten.
Instead of being the Very
Most Top Person in Europe the
Emperor William had to run away
and hide and never be an Important Person any more.

You know that for Ages and Ages the men of Great Britain
had been allowed to choose Members for Parliament. Every Man
who paid enough Taxes was allowed to make a Mark on a bit of
Paper which meant, "This is the Person I want to be my Member
of Parliament." That was called having a Vote.

It was only Men who were allowed to have a Vote. Women
weren't allowed to. But for a long time Women had been trying
hard to make the men see how Unfair that was. "We pay Taxes,"
they said, "so we ought to be allowed to help to choose our
Members of Parliament. If we're not to be allowed to do that we
shouldn't be made to pay Taxes."

But the Top Persons in Parliament wouldn't listen to Reason.
They just laughed and said, "Oh, nonsense. If we let you choose
Members of Parliament you'll want to be Members next."

"Well, why not?" asked the women.

"What a Dreadful Idea," said the Top Persons. "We certainly
couldn't stand that," and they wouldn't listen to anything the
women said.

Then some of the women got wild. They began doing Mad
Things and even Bad Things just to make the Top Persons as
Uncomfortable as they could, and pay them back for not listening.

Probably in time the Top Persons would have got so Uncomfortable that they'd have Given In. But before anything got settled the Dreadful War began. So of course the Women gave up thinking about getting the Vote and began working hard for the Good-of-the-Country. Then all the Nice Men said, "Just look at what the Women have done. We couldn't have got on without them. Of course they must have the Vote." So they got it. Now women can help to choose their Members of Parliament just the same as the Men. And they can Be Members of Parliament too just the same as Men.

Years went by and King George sat on the Throne doing the best he could for his People. Then when he'd been sitting on the Throne for twenty-five years the Sad News was flashed all through his great Empire, "The King is dead."

Then once again the People felt dreadfully, dreadfully sad. They felt sad for themselves for they had lost a King and a Friend. They felt sad for Queen Mary too, for she had lost her dear Husband.

Edward VIII. A Very Sad "Goodbye"

Edward Prince of Wales now became King. We'd known and loved him long before he began to do the Ruling. For when he was Prince of Wales he was always going about Doing Things *and* thinking about the Good-of-the-People and how to make them Happy and Comfortable.

They knew him so well, and liked him so much, that they just called him "The Prince," as if he were the only Prince in all the Wide World.

Like Edward III and Henry VII too, he took a great Interest in the Trade-of-the-Country, and went about finding out the Best Ways of doing things. So he got called "Our Royal Commercial Traveller."

But Edward VIII was never Crowned. He wished to marry a Lady that many of the Top Best People all over the Empire thought would not make a Good Queen.

"Very well," said King Edward, "I'd rather be with my Lady than be the Ruler of this Great Empire. So I'll go away and not be your King any more. But you needn't be Sad and Sorry about it, because I have a Very Nice Brother who will make a Very Good King."

They were Very Sad and Sorry. But it couldn't be helped. So they just said, "Goodbye, and God Bless You."

And King Edward said, "Goodbye, and God Bless you."

Then he went away to be with his Dear Lady. So then he wasn't called His Majesty King Edward any more but His Royal Highness the Duke of Windsor.

George VI. Not All a Fairy-Tale

What King Edward VIII said was quite true. He had a Very Nice Brother and he became our Very Good King George VI. He had a lovely Wife too, called Queen Elizabeth, and two daughters called Princess Elizabeth and Princess Margaret.

Then a Very Sad and Bad Thing happened. The people of Germany came under the rule of a Really Bad Man who thought he could make Germany the strongest state in the Whole World.

And so a Second World War began. It lasted for six years, and though Germany was beaten and its Wicked Ruler lost his life, the World was left in a Dreadful Mess again.

Our Beloved King was a Great Help to his people during all this Bad Time, and all the Top People who were fighting in the War or were working at home were glad that at the Head of them all was such a Wise and Kind Ruler. Everyone in the land loved him and his Family.

But though he made no Fuss about himself he became very ill. Everyone was very sorry about this, and the Doctors did their best to cure him. But one morning the Dreadful News came that he was dead. He had died peacefully in his sleep. Everyone knew that he had given his life for his People as he had Made Up His Mind to do at the very beginning.

Queen Elizabeth II

The beautiful Princess Elizabeth now became Queen Elizabeth. There had been a Queen Elizabeth in England before, and she had had a Glorious Reign. Now the People of the Whole Country and the Great Commonwealth, of which the new Queen is the Head, hoped and prayed that this Reign also would be just as Glorious and Great.

A FEW DATES

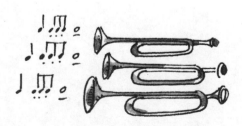